THE FIRST
50 years

ssembly area in Cedar Rapids in 1973. The lines from the ceiling supplied electricity and compressed air to the work stations.

T H E   F I R S T

50 years

A History of Collins Radio Company and the Collins Divisions of Rockwell International

By Ken C. Braband

With excerpts from articles by:
Dr. R.L. Carrel, Arlo Goodyear, Tony Huebsch, Gerald Ozburn, Horst
Schweighofer, John Staehle, and Ben Stearns.

Acknowledgments

Research assistance by Rebecca Gregory.

Special thanks to John Goetz, Milo Soukup, Richard Pickering, John Nyquist, and Rick Plummer for their guidance and research assistance.

Thanks to the following for contributing to this project:

For technical and historical assistance: William Anderson, Don Buss, Russell Colton, Dennis Day, Harold Ewoldt, Irvin H. Gerks, C. F. Hardenbrook, Gertrude Harrison, Mary Henningson, Tony Huebsch, Bridgette Janus at the *Cedar Rapids Gazette,* Ruth Jurgens at the City Clerk's office, Millie Lahr, Clayton Lander, George Lippisch, Evelyn Lyon, J. Bruce Majerus, Joyce Mansfield, Robert Maresh, Pat Marshall, Jim Miller, Gordon Nicholson, Alvin Oujiri, Leonard Peters, Bob Pierce, J. Patrick Riley, Al Snodgrass, R. J. Tibor, and Kathy Zeller.

For production assistance: Dave Berner, Ernie Danek, Al Evans, Diana Fairchild, Vickie Kintzel, Jack Miller, Marlin Petersen, Melanie Rice, Wilma Shadle, Mary Williams, and Robert Woods.

Bernie Gish and Al Wolfe at the company archives, Judy Leavitt and the staff of the Collins Information Center, Townsend Hoopes III for writing the "Helicopter Autopilot" and "Special Lady" stories, Ray Walsh for writing the "Collision Avoidance" story, John Giordano for preparing the product history chart, Patricia Cram, Marcia Clemmens, and Chris Riley for proofreading, and the Collins photo lab for making pictures from all those old oversize negatives.

Thanks also to members of the 50th Anniversary Steering Committee, whose support made this project possible. Committee members: Cheryl Anderson, Richard Fredericks, Ted Gedicke, Townsend Hoopes III, and Trudy Michel.

Designed and printed by Stamats Communications, Inc., Cedar Rapids, Iowa. Richard Braley, design director; Thomas Jackson, jacket design; Patricia Garcia, primary designer and coordinator; Gail Malmanger, design assistant; Michael Hunstad, design intern; Jack Hines, project coordinator; Dawn Erb, creative services coordinator.

Jacket artwork scenes by Mayo Olmstead

The first Collins trademark, used in 1933, was a globe with lines of longitude and latitude and two long, slim wings extending from it. The idea was submitted by a Cedar Rapids firm for a letterhead on the first company stationery.

The following year, the same idea reappeared with the grids removed, the globe enlarged and shaded, and wings shortened.

By the 1940s, the Collins name was prominently displayed in a redesigned trademark which replaced the wings with straight lines.

In 1961, a new trademark was produced by Ken Parkhurst & Associates of Los Angeles. The symbol was patterned after widening circles caused by dropping a pebble into a pond.

After the acquisition of Collins by Rockwell International in 1973, the Collins divisions adopted the trademark of the parent corporation.

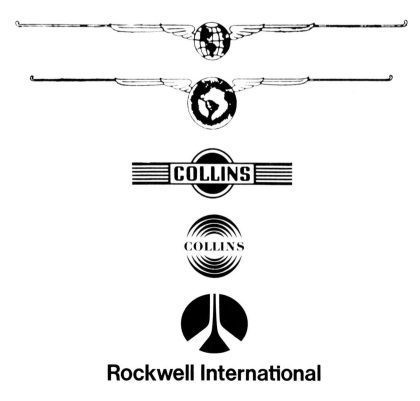

Early in the 19th century, an English physicist, Michael Faraday, demonstrated that an electric current produced a local magnetic field and that the energy in the field returned to the circuit when the current was stopped or changed.

In 1864, James Clerk Maxwell used mathematical formulas to prove that any electrical disturbance could produce an effect a long distance away. Maxwell predicted that electromagnetic energy could travel as waves moving at the speed of light.

It was not until about 1888 that Maxwell's theory was tested by Heinrich Hertz. Hertz demonstrated that Maxwell's predictions were true, at least over short distances, by installing a spark gap at the center of a parabolic mirror. Another spark gap was placed about five feet away at the focus of another parabolic collector in line with the first. A spark jumping across the first gap caused a smaller spark to jump across the gap five feet away. Hertz showed that the waves traveled in a straight line and that they could be reflected by a metal sheet just as light waves are reflected by a mirror.

The Italian physicist Guglielmo Marconi refused to accept the common belief that electromagnetic waves could not travel beyond the horizon. Marconi repeated Hertz's experiments and eventually succeeded in getting secondary sparks over a distance of 300 yards, then two miles, then across the English Channel. Finally in 1901, Marconi stirred the imagination of the scientific world when he transmitted the letter ''s'' in Morse code across the Atlantic Ocean from Cornwall, England, to St. John's, Newfoundland, a distance of nearly 2,000 miles.

Other developments in radio progress came quickly in the early years of the 20th century. Sir John Ambrose Fleming explored the phenomenon of a unidirectional current effect between a positive electrode and a heated filament in a vacuum tube. Fleming called his device a diode because it contained two electrodes. Fleming's discovery was the first step to the amplifier tube, which in the early part of the 20th century revolutionized radio communication.

Fleming did not fully appreciate the possibilities he had opened up, and it was the Waterloo, Iowa-born inventor Lee De Forest who in 1906 placed an open-meshed metal grid between the heated filament and the positively-charged electrode, or plate, to control the flow of electrons. De Forest called his invention the Audion. It was a major advancement because it made possible amplification of the radio-frequency signal picked up by the antenna before it was sent to the receiver detector. The result — much weaker signals than previously possible could be used.

As research into this new means of communication progressed, commercial interest followed. The first commercial company to be incorporated for the manufacture of radio apparatus was the Wireless Telegraph and Signal Company, Ltd. of England in 1897 (later changed to Marconi's Wireless Telegraph Company, Ltd.). The large American Telephone & Telegraph Company led the effort to transmit speech by radio. All previous radio achievements had used the dots and dashes of Morse code. In 1915, AT&T successfully transmitted speech signals from west to east across the Atlantic between Arlington, Virginia, and Paris.

In 1916, David Sarnoff, then contracts manager to the American Marconi company, recommended that transmitting stations be built to broadcast speech and music, and that a "radio music box" should be manufactured for general sale. His proposals were not immediately implemented, partly because of America's entry into World War I in 1917, but they proved highly practical. The first regular broadcasting station was KDKA in Pittsburgh, which started operations in 1920. The service gained instant popularity, and the idea quickly spread around the world. By 1925 there were more than 500 broadcast stations in the United States alone.

Manufacturers of radio receivers sprouted across the country. The largest were located in the east: Harrison Radio Company, Baltimore Radio Corporation, Radio Corporation of America (RCA) Victor Co., Inc., American Telephone and Telegraph, General Electric, Westinghouse, and Pilot Radio and Tube Corporation.

Occasionally amidst the enthusiasm for this marvelous new system of popular entertainment and information, stories were heard of amateur radio operators, who with their own home-built equipment and with power of only a few watts, had established communication with other amateurs in distant parts of the world. They used the part of the radio spectrum known as shortwaves, which were regarded as of no use for commercial purposes and had been given to the amateurs to play with.

C O N T E N T S

1

A young radio enthusiast

Early amateur radio operators were mainly hobbyists, but there was a sense of discovery during the infancy of radio that provided something more. Radio was the new thing, comparable to what computers mean to technological whizzes in the 1980s. And like the computer hobbyists of today who are writing their own programs and building their own equipment, amateur radio operators in the 1920s were contributing to the knowledge of practical aspects of radio art.

One person caught up in the excitement of radio was Arthur Andrew Collins.

Born in Kingfisher, Oklahoma, on Sept. 9, 1909, Collins moved to Cedar Rapids, Iowa, at an early age when his father, Merle (or M. H. as he preferred to see it written), established The Collins Farms Company there.

With the Collins Farms Company, M. H. Collins brought new ideas to the stoic profession of farming. The elder Collins reasoned that the efforts of scientists and engineers could do for farming what they did for nearly every other industry in America.

"Why not manufacture food for the American consumer as cheaply as motor cars and radios are manufactured?" M. H. asked in a publication which explained his new ideas. "Why not produce food on a large scale by intensive farming methods in Iowa, where high yields could be obtained and at a low cost?"

The primary object of the farm company was to produce grain at low cost. M. H. Collins felt that too many farmers mixed grain production with livestock raising, and as a result, both were unprofitable.

He implemented his plans by convincing landowners he could improve the profitability of their tenant farms. Farms of 160 to 320 acres were planted to a single crop and were rotated as a single tract in a unit group of farms, each embracing 1,500 to 2,000 acres. Each unit of contiguous farms was put under the supervision of a salaried foreman who directed the tractor operators. The most modern machinery was employed for every operation — four-row cultivators, rotary

The variety of radio magazines testified to the popularity of the hobby in the 1920s.

One of the modern implements used by the Collins Farm Company was a "cultipacker" which pulverized and firmed the seed bed. Note the electric lights on the tractor, another innovation.

hoes, deep disc plows, two-row corn pickers, fast trucks for marketing crops, and semi-trailers for moving machinery. For maximum use of all this new machinery, electric lights were placed on the tractors, allowing round-the-clock operation. Other practices initiated by The Collins Farms Company included installing drainage tile, erecting fire-proof ventilated grain storage bins, and using legumes to replace nitrogen in the soil.

At its peak the company operated 60,000 acres of farmland in 31 Iowa counties, with wealthy businessman M. H. Collins at the helm of the corporation.

At about the age of nine, Arthur Collins became deeply interested in the new marvel of radio, although at first M. H. apparently did not think highly of his son's tinkerings with radio. Arthur and another early boyhood radio devotee, Merrill Lund, made their first crystal receivers at the Lund home at 1644 D Avenue in Cedar Rapids. The sets used variable condensers inside a tube. Merrill's father worked in the tube department at Quaker Oats Co. and made tubes of the size the boys needed. Using thumb tacks for contact points, they wrapped wire around the tubes. From iron plates they fashioned their own transformers, and rigged a 60-foot spark antenna with a lead-in through a basement window of the Lund home. Merrill's father asked them to find another location for their equipment after lightning struck the radio set and blew it up.

Arthur brought over two coaster wagons and the two boys transported the damaged equipment to the Collins home at 1725 Grande Avenue. Although M. H. did not approve of the mess it was going to cause, Arthur hauled the equipment to his room once his father was out of sight.

"I used a Quaker Oats box to wind the tuning coil and used a Model T spark coil," he told a *New York Times* reporter in 1962. "The main piece of the station's machinery was the transmitter. Other parts of the station were recruited from a rural telephone service. The way we calibrated was to pick up signals from WWV (the Navy's station in Arlington, Virginia)."

Arthur also used pieces of coal or coke for a rectifier, glass towel racks for insulators and a toy motor. Those early efforts reflected a lot of experimenting that led to successively more reliable, higher-performance radios.

Another boyhood friend in Cedar Rapids who also had an interest in radio was Clair Miller.

"Arthur had big expensive tubes as a kid while all the rest of us had were peanut tubes," Miller told a reporter in 1965.

The article quoted another neighbor's recollection of early days in the Collins family neighborhood: "We sensed that Arthur was different, but we did not know that he was a genius. When the rest of us were out playing cowboy and Indian, Arthur was in the house working on his radios."

One day Arthur's mother invited the neighborhood boys into the Collins home. "I think she did so because she wanted us to realize that Arthur was different from the rest of us. We went upstairs to see what he was doing. He had a room that overlooked the yard. It was loaded with radio stuff. We knew a little about radio. We had been playing around with crystal sets ourselves. But Arthur had one wall covered with dials and switches, everything under the sun."

The Federal Radio Commission, the predecessor to the Federal Communications Commission, passed a radio act whereby amateurs could get licenses. Arthur took the test and got his license in 1923 at the age of 14.

As M. H. Collins recognized his son's talent and ambition toward radio, he looked for ways to help with Arthur's hobby. In about 1924, Arthur's father purchased a new tube costing $135 and other high voltage equipment.

"When I was a youngster there were two real active amateurs (in Cedar Rapids)," Arthur recalled. "One was Henry Nemec and the other was Clark Chandler." Collins and Leo Hruska, another friend who had constructed a crystal receiver, used to receive the stations of Nemec and Chandler, and considered their talks with the more experienced radio operators quite an achievement.

Nemec recalled how he first met the young boy with the extensive radio knowledge. M. H. Collins had asked Nemec to meet with his son so Nemec could teach Arthur some of what he knew about amateur radio, "But there wasn't much that he didn't already know," Nemec said.

In a 1978 interview for an article about Henry Nemec in the *Cedar Rapids Gazette,* Arthur Collins recalled the early days when he purchased a vacuum tube from Nemec, and several years later when Nemec, who worked for the police department, and another patrolman, Frank Bukacek, parked their squad car in front of Collins' house while the three were inside talking radio. Collins said he, Nemec and Bukacek got together so frequently, and the squad car was parked in front of the house so often, that neighbors began to wonder whether Collins was in some kind of trouble with the police.

At the time there was little formal instruction in the science of radio. Several two-day short courses were given at Iowa State College at Ames, and Arthur is said to have attended the first of these while still wearing knickers. Carl Mentzer later sponsored a course in radio at the University of Iowa. These courses, along with several periodicals, including *Wireless Age* and *QST,* comprised most of the current radio knowledge of the time, other than word-of-mouth information.

By the time he was a teenager, Arthur had constructed an amateur radio station using purchased components, makeshift materials and his own ingenuity. Arthur's family had moved to a new home at 514 Fairview Drive, and his equipment moved with him.

By the age of 15, Collins had communicated with other amateur "hams" in the United States and many foreign countries. The custom of exchanging postcards after a contact was made had already been established in the amateur world, and one wall of Collins' attic room was covered with so-called QSL cards.

One card from Australia came from a radio operator who regarded America's prohibition of alcohol as a joke.

"How does it feel to stay sober?" were the words the Australian ham wrote to 15-year-old Arthur.

And during a contact with a person in Chile, the South American operator asked to be excused from the radio conversation because a volcano was erupting and interfering with the talk. "He referred to it as if it was in his backyard," Collins told a *Cedar Rapids Gazette* reporter in 1925.

The reporter, Gladys Arne, had gone to the Collins home

This highly-retouched photograph of 15-year-old Arthur Collins originally appeared in the August 11, 1925 Cedar Rapids Gazette. The sloping walls of the attic at 514 Fairview Drive held many of the QSL postcards Collins received from other "ham" radio enthusiasts.

to talk with the 15-year-old boy because he had made a radio contact that put him on the front pages of newspapers all over the country.

During the winter of 1924-25, Collins had become familiar with John Reinartz, a 31-year-old German immigrant who was prominent in radio circles because he developed a "tuner" or receiver capable of predictable selectivity and reception. Reinartz had authored several articles on the subject for radio magazines. Reinartz and Collins carried on experiments, particularly in the use of short wavelengths.

Because of Reinartz's radio success, he was chosen as the radio operator for a scientific expedition to the continent of Greenland. The MacMillan expedition set sail from the coast of Maine on the ships *Bowdoin* and *Perry* in early 1925. One of the explorers was U.S. Navy Lt. Cdr. Richard E. Byrd.

The plan was for the *Bowdoin* to make daily radio reports to the U.S. Naval radio station, but because of atmospheric problems, the land station in Washington, D.C., was unable to consistently receive Reinartz's messages.

Then word spread that a 15-year-old boy in Cedar Rapids had made contact with the expedition.

Throughout the summer of 1925, Arthur Collins accomplished a task that even the U.S. Navy found difficult. Using a ham radio that he himself had built, he talked by code with Reinartz in Greenland night after night. His signals reached the expedition more clearly than any other. After each broadcast, young Collins took the messages from the expedition down to the Cedar Rapids telegraph office and relayed to Washington the scientific findings that the exploratory group had uncovered that day.

Collins' exclusive contact with the expedition soon became a nationwide news story that won him acclaim as a radio wizard. The August 4, 1925 *Cedar Rapids Gazette* told the story:

"The mysterious forces of air leaped the boundary of thousands of miles to bring Cedar Rapids in touch with the celebrated MacMillan scientific expedition at Etah, Greenland, and wrote a new chapter into the history of radio. Sunday, Arthur Collins, 514 Fairview Drive, 15-year-old radio wizard, picked up the message from the expedition's ship Bowdoin, at twenty meters (wavelength), at about 3 o'clock and conversed in continental code for more than one hour. It was the first time the expedition and any United States radio station had communicated at that wavelength. Messages were received by Collins for the National Geographic Society, which is sponsoring the expedition, and for others, and were sent out from here by telegraph. Arthur Collins is the son of Mr. and Mrs. M. H. Collins and is a student at Washington High School. He has been a radio fan for years, and has himself constructed most of his apparatus. His equipment is in a small room on the third floor of the Collins home. His station is known as 9CXX. The local boy told a *Gazette* reporter today that although he had been in wireless communication with Australia, Scotland, England, India, Puerto Rico, Guam, and Mexico, he never had received a greater thrill than when he talked to his friend on the famous expedition bound northward to explore a mystic continent."

One week later, a follow-up article in the *Gazette* concluded: "Though only 15, he is true to his trust. For he hopes to realize great radio ambitions, by and by."

At the age of 16, Collins was asked to write a technical article for *Radio Age* which was published in the May, 1926, issue. One statement in that article foreshadowed the motivational force which was to lead him to "great radio ambitions."

"The real thrill in amateur work comes not from talking to stations in distant lands . . . but from knowing that by careful and painstaking work and by diligent and systematic study

Before departing for the southwest, the operators of 9ZZA posed with their mobile shortwave station. From left: Winfield Salisbury, Paul Engle, and Arthur Collins.

you have been able to accomplish some feat, or establish some fact that is a new step toward more perfect communication."

Arthur's reputation in the radio world grew. Radio operators around the country who had heard about his contacts with the MacMillan expedition wrote to him to ask how he did it.

Collins continued his electronics education by taking courses at Amherst College in Massachusetts, Coe College in Cedar Rapids, and the University of Iowa in Iowa City.

In 1927, he and two friends organized an expedition of sorts of their own. Collins, Paul Engle, and Winfield Salisbury outfitted a truck with short wave transmitting and receiving equipment and took a summer trip to the southwest states. Using power of 10 watts they conducted experiments in connection with the U.S. Naval Observatory in Washington, D.C. Leo Hruska stayed behind in Cedar Rapids to operate the base station for the study.

Like Collins, both Engle and Salisbury would later go on to achieve recognition in their particular chosen fields — Engle as a poet and professor at the University of Iowa, and Salisbury as a noted physicist who would make significant contributions to studies initiated by Collins.

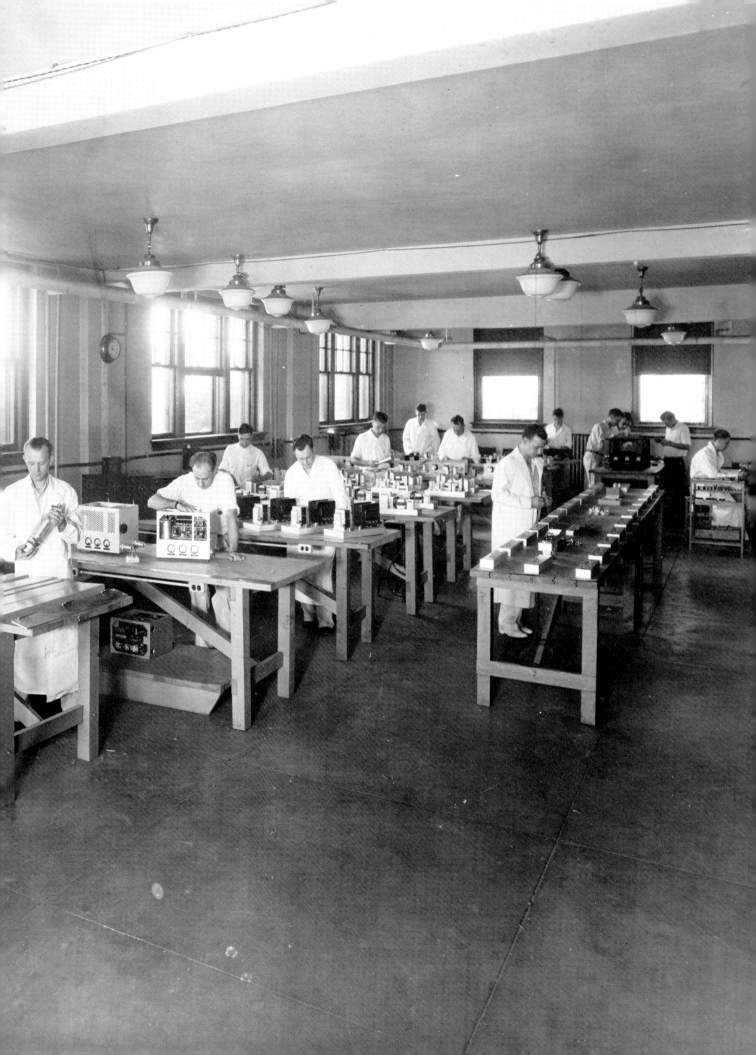

2

Up from the cellar

I n 1930, Collins married Margaret Van Dyke. By the end of 1931 he had set up a shop in the basement of their home at 1620 6th Avenue S.E., previously the home of his grandparents. Arthur began to produce transmitters to order.

When the depression hit with full force in 1931, 23-year-old Collins turned his hobby into a vocation.

"I picked what I was interested in," he told *Forbes* magazine years later, "and looked for a way to make a living."

This was the first time radio transmitting apparatus, of any power output, was available for purchase as an assembled and working unit. In fact, components were hard to come by; they varied widely in characteristics, and there was little, if any, pattern to their construction. Most hams had their radio equipment scattered around a room, usually in a basement or attic where the sight of tubes and wires wouldn't clutter up living areas of a home. Their equipment was strictly functional, almost to the point of inefficiency.

Collins' ham gear was designed to eliminate the clutter by packaging the equipment in neat units. The concept proved that correctly engineered construction not only stabilized the circuitry but also made its behavior predictable. Collins designed circuits, fabricated chassis, mounted and wired in components, tested, packed and shipped each unit. Because

Left
The assembly area at 2920 First Avenue as it appeared in 1934. Workers were identified, from left, as: Elmer Koehn, Don Anderson, Don Holmes, Don Wheaton, Roy Olson, John Dayhoff, Arlo Goodyear, Don Cole, Don Andersen, R. E. Samuelson, Walt Wirkler, Leonard Braun, and Gerald Ozburn.

Near Right
The basement of this home at 1620 6th Avenue SE was the first factory in which Arthur Collins produced radio transmitters to order.

Far Right
One of the earliest advertisements placed by Arthur Collins appeared in the September, 1932 issue of QST, a magazine for amateur radio hobbyists.

A manual is now available describing COLLINS transmitters, speech equipment, condenser microphones and transformers, complete with full specifications and circuit diagrams.

Send 25c in coin

COLLINS RADIO TRANSMITTERS
W9CXX, CEDAR RAPIDS, IOWA

the gear was precisely engineered and well-built with the best parts available, it gave years of trouble-free service.

A later article in the *New York Times* quoted a ham as saying, "Collins brought us up from the cellar and put us into the living room." The industrial philosophy of Collins products — quality — was established at the very start.

The first advertisement for this new line of products appeared in the January, 1932 issue of *QST,* with the firm name given as Arthur A. Collins. Two issues later, in March, 1932, the firm name appeared as Collins Radio Transmitters with Arthur's name and call number below. Both notices were two-inch advertisements, but by May the size was increased to six inches. In October the first full-page ad appeared and by December, the firm's name was listed as Collins Radio Company.

Long-time friend Jiggs Ozburn recalled his first meeting with Collins.

"I first met Arthur Collins at a ham club meeting at his house (factory in basement). I hadn't finished high school and he hadn't finished college (he never did). Art had been making ham transmitters for about a year. He was tall and slender and very quiet. He came from a well-to-do family whose fortune was taking a beating in those depression years, so Art was pretty much on his own."

The Great Depression, which began after the stock market crash in 1929, was having a devastating effect on the Collins Farms Company. In 1931, M. H. Collins sold the firm to an east coast insurance company.

Arthur originally started his company as sole owner with only one employee, Clair Miller, who had just been graduated from Iowa State College. But as his business grew, he added personnel, including some who came from his father's farm company. Among them were John Dayhoff and Ted Saxon.

Orders came in and the company grew. In 1933, Collins Radio Company moved out of the basement factory and into leased space at 2920 First Avenue in Cedar Rapids, now headquarters for the local Salvation Army.

Business in general in 1933 was not good, to put it mildly, but radio had come of age, and Collins recognized the need for advancement in the radio communications field.

One Saturday morning that year, Collins telephoned Arlo Goodyear and offered him a job for two months if he was willing to work on Sundays. Out of work for months and with a wife and baby, Goodyear jumped at the opportunity.

"There it was in the middle of the Depression and he was asking me if I minded working on Sunday," Goodyear later

The basement of this building at 2920 First Avenue became the factory and office area for Collins Radio Co. in 1933.

A tale of an early sale

Reprinted by permission, *CQ Magazine,* August, 1965.

By Ed Marriner

A Sunday afternoon during the hot, humid Iowa summer is usually not conducive to much activity except relaxing or recreation. The often oppressive heat and sunshine place a mantle of stillness over the landscape, broken only by a gentle breeze.

Such was the case back in 1932 when Benton White and his wife were driving through the Iowa countryside. The heat and weariness from travel led them to call a halt and find a hotel room to cool off. Passing a newsstand, Benton noticed a QST magazine which he picked up, casually glancing through the pages. By chance his eyes fell on an ad for "Collins Transmitters" made in Cedar Rapids by Arthur A. Collins.

With nothing more important to do, Benton decided to locate the Collins factory even if it was a Sunday afternoon.

Returning to the hotel to get his wife, they drove around town with her as navigator until they arrived at the given address, a house on a quiet shady street. Despite her protests, "You must be mistaken, there is no factory here," Benton decided to ring the doorbell anyway and see for himself.

A lady answered the door and replied to his question, "Yes, this is the Collins factory. Just a minute and I will call Mr. Collins." Benton returned to the car to inform his wife that he would be inside for awhile.

As he again approached the house he overheard a man talking on the telephone to a Mr. Miller and urging him to hurry over, saying "I think we have a customer." Benton had no intention of buying anything that Sunday afternoon, and as he silently debated whether to go through with his visit a jalopy pulled up outside with a squeal of brakes. Before he could change his mind, Benton was whisked inside and down into the basement; the Collins factory.

In one corner stood the furnace, a cat curled up next to the cool steel base. Around the walls were neat, clean workbenches. On one bench was a nearly completed transmitter, and as the three men gathered around it, Mr. Collins and his associate, the only other employee of the firm at the time, fired up soldering irons and started working.

Benton recalled that as members of the ham fraternity they sat on stools and chatted. He was impressed with the transmitter as a high quality piece of gear, which he decided then and there he wanted for his own.

Informed that the transmitter was being built for someone else, Benton nevertheless was able to negotiate an immediate deal when he produced on the spot the $97.50 which was the price.

Everything was apparently working out just as Mr. Collins and his partner had planned, and in a short time the three of them were loading the transmitter in Benton's car so he could take it home to Chattanooga, Tenn.

It is believed this was the first or second full-sized transmitter, not a kit, which the Collins company sold, and a forerunner of thousands of Collins electronic units used for many applications throughout the world.

Down through the years the transmitter remained a treasured possession of Benton White, complete in its original condition except for replacement of a condenser. He operated the transmitter for a good many years until it became semi-retired as a low power emergency and field day rig.

Several years ago Mr. White died. The story of this incident was related by Harry Heilbeck, and brought to the attention of Mr. Collins. With a brief lead, the Collins company started to track down the early production transmitter. It had changed hands since the death of Benton, but was located and arrangements were made to obtain it for an amateur equipment display room at the Collins plant in Cedar Rapids.

wrote. "I would have worked on Shrove Tuesday."

Collins and his work force of one arrived at the building only to discover that neither had a key to get into the basement area, where the company was to begin production the next morning.

Collins looked at the door, looked at Goodyear, and said, "Well, we've got to get going. Catch me so I won't fall on my head." Collins charged the locked door and the new plant got underway with a bang and a shattered front door.

Corporation Formed

On September 22, 1933, with eight employees and $29,000 in capital, Collins Radio Company became a corporation under the laws of the State of Delaware.

At that time Delaware had some of the most modern corporation laws in the country, and many businesses were officially organizing there, although their actual facilities were located in other states. (On May 13, 1937, the company reorganized as an Iowa corporation.)

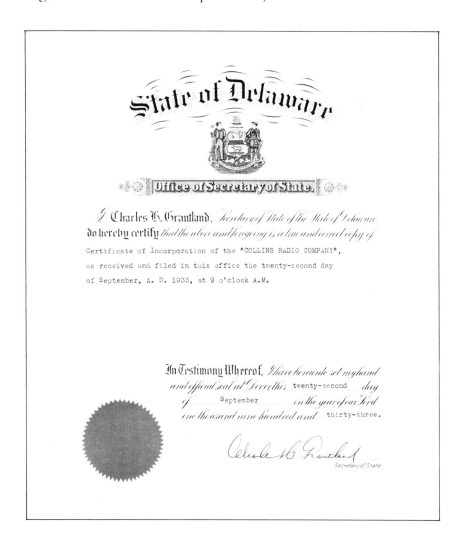

The original document of incorporation listed the time as 9 a.m., September 22, 1933.

The first meeting of the board of directors of Collins Radio was held at the new First Avenue location on October 10, 1933. The entire board of directors was present: Arthur Collins; his wife, Margaret; his father, M. H.; and his mother, Faith. Arthur was elected president, and M. H. was made vice president of the new corporation. Also present was Irene Snyder, who was elected secretary and treasurer.

Originally 250 shares of stock were issued for the company, which was given an arbitrary book value of $20,746. Of these shares, 124 each were issued to Margaret and Faith Collins and one share each to Arthur and M. H. Collins.

During the first two years, Collins Radio built only four types of transmitters, all designed for the amateur radio market.

But the reputation of the small firm grew, and Collins found that his equipment was being put to use by government and commercial enterprises as well.

However, outside the world of radio few people knew much about the new company, even in Cedar Rapids.

Jiggs Ozburn recalled that when Collins was called upon to install a new high fidelity system at Cedar Park, the dance bands that played there "made fun of our little (then new on the market) crystal microphone, saying it was just 'a crummy single button carbon mike.' At this time the city of Cedar Rapids was hardly aware of Collins Radio."

Another incident which pointed out Collins Radio Company's anonymity in the early days is told by long-time employee Millie Lahr.

"My brother, Albert Fay Rathbun, worked for a freight company. He was to deliver some parts to someone by the name of Arthur Collins in a basement and he was told to be sure to collect freight charges, because it was probably some fly-by-night outfit."

The big break
Late in 1933, a series of events began that would again put Arthur Collins in the national limelight, and assure his infant company a thriving childhood.

Most of Boston was still sleeping that October morning when a freighter of World War I vintage, the *Jacob Ruppert,* slipped from its moorings, inched cautiously through the harbor's mist and sailed southward into history.

Crammed into the radio shack of the ship was communication gear that would keep the 115-man expedition in contact with the rest of the world.

The destination — the South Pole. The man in charge — Admiral Richard E. Byrd. The same Richard Byrd who

Upper
Arthur Collins, president of Collins Radio Company, 1934.

Lower
M. H. Collins, vice president of Collins Radio, 1934.

14

In a room called the design laboratory, engineer Roy Olson worked at the table and Leonard Vick manned the drafting board. (1934)

learned about Arthur Collins from the Arctic in 1925 had become Rear Admiral Richard Byrd by 1933. The radio equipment — supplied by Collins Radio Company.

The black electronic boxes served as much more than a means of communication for Byrd. They played an unusual role as "fundraisers" for his second expedition to the Antarctic.

After CBS officials investigated the technical hazards of broadcasting from an area of the world well-known for the havoc it played with radio transmissions, they decided to risk underwriting the project, and commissioned the Collins Radio Company to design and build the transmitters and accessories.

Just eight years earlier the nation had read how a 15-year-old boy kept in daily contact with MacMillan's Arctic expedition. Five years later, in 1930, Collins again made communication news when his equipment provided continual contact with Admiral Byrd's first expedition to the Antarctic. For those two trips, the means of communication was shortwave radio telegraph. Because of the tremendous distances it was necessary to cover with relatively low-power equipment, the

15

1

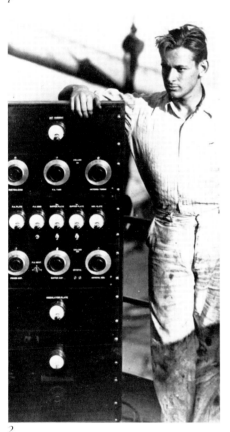

2

3

4

5

6

7

For his Antarctic expeditions, Richard Byrd employed the latest devices available to explorers — shortwave radio and airplanes.

Opposite Page
Rear Admiral Richard E. Byrd.

This Page
1
The workhorse of the 1933 expedition, a Curtiss-Wright Condor, was carried aboard the Jacob Ruppert *and lowered to the water for take-offs. The pontoons could easily be replaced with aluminum skis for snow and ice operation.*

2
Guy Hutcheson, radio operator on the Jacob Ruppert *posed with one of the 150B transmitters used as an exciter to drive the larger 20B transmitter. The 150B also drove the antenna direct when full power was not needed.*

3
The main radio room aboard the Jacob Ruppert *was crowded with transmitters, receivers and amplifiers.*

4
Broadcasts to the United States usually originated in other quarters, so crew members had room to gather around the microphones.

5
After mooring at the ice shelf, supplies were transported by dogsled, motorized snow vehicles, and airplane.

6
One member of the expedition prepares his gear for a trek on skis. The antenna in the background was one used for transmissions from Little America.

7
Collins received this telegram from Byrd as the expedition sailed toward the South Pole.

17

only radio was the more reliable dot-dash coded method of radio telegraphy.

But by 1933, advancement in shortwave radio voice communication (or radio telephony as it was called) was so great that Byrd decided to take radio telephony equipment along to the South Pole.

The attempt was a gamble, for if it failed, the reputations of the expedition, CBS, and Collins Radio Company would suffer.

"It was a costly gamble for everyone if it failed," Byrd later wrote, "for involved was a 10,000-mile radio telephone circuit and expensive amplification relay set-ups — all from our ships and a shore station incapable of powering a transmitter with much better than a peanut-stand strength compared to the power in a large broadcasting station."

A careful study of the technical problems involved was made by Dr. T. S. McCaleb of Harvard University, director of communications for the expedition, and E. K. Cohan, technical director of CBS. So great was their faith in the plan and in the Collins equipment they had selected, CBS sold the proposed broadcasts to a prominent advertiser, General Foods Corp., so they would be heard not only by amateurs and shortwave listeners, but by the vast radio broadcast audience over the nationwide CBS network.

Major problems had to be overcome to make the plan work.

First was the limitation imposed by the source of power available. Consideration of fuel consumption for generators and weight limited the size of the transmitter which could be used. The commercial transoceanic transmitters of the day used 40 or 50 kilowatts output to maintain consistent communication. The study team found that the job would have to be done with a one-kilowatt transmitter.

Another problem was the antenna aboard the ship. Commercial ground stations used directional antennas covering acres of ground to concentrate as much of the signal as possible toward the receiving station. The inefficient antenna on the *Jacob Ruppert* would have to be used until the expedition reached Little America in the Antarctic.

The largest problem to overcome was the varying transmission conditions which affect shortwaves. Magnetic storms occasionally interrupted commercial circuits for days at a time.

But with these things firmly in mind, the engineers of the Byrd expedition went ahead with their plans.

Collins Radio Company shipped a large, one-kilowatt Type 20B transmitter to Boston for use as the main link with the

United States. In addition, two smaller Collins 150B transmitters were used for communication between the different camps of the expedition.

Martin Kahn, Collins field engineer, assisted in installation onboard the *Jacob Ruppert* and accompanied the expedition from Boston to New York.

The first broadcast was made on November 11, 1933, from a position near Easter Island off the coast of Chili. The program was picked up in New York and placed on the network at the appointed hour. The CBS engineers at New York and the operators aboard the ship had been carrying out daily tests for two weeks, but this was the real test. As luck would have it, conditions were miserable. The *Jacob Ruppert* was in a heavy sea and the speakers had trouble keeping the proper spacing from the microphone because of the rolling of the ship. Nevertheless, the program came through understandably, although somewhat distorted by fading and background noise. Astonished broadcast listeners were thrilled when they heard the flagship's whistle, an introduction of various members of the expedition, the barking of the 150 huskies aboard the ship, and an announcement by Rear Admiral Byrd himself.

Later broadcasts were made from other positions in the South Pacific as the expedition journeyed on its way to Antarctica.

On February 3, 1934, Byrd prepared for the first formal broadcast from the Antarctic continent.

"We gathered in the Old Mess Hall by the dim light of kerosene lanterns. Hutcheson fiddled with controls, on a monitor board. He snapped his fingers across the microphones to test them. And I thought, as I watched these mysterious preparations, how broadly things had changed, how 22 years before, Scott and his whole party had silently died of hunger while his base, just 160 miles away, awaited his homecoming at Cape Evans, and here we were casually making ready to tell of our prosaic days to a vast audience in the United States. A thing called a cue came through. Each of us went to the microphone to say his piece and 10,000 miles away our voices came through clear as a bell. Somewhere in the shadow of the mess hall, 15 feet below the surface, it didn't seem possible."

Later, broadcasts were made on a weekly basis from Antarctica, and by July members of the expedition succeeded in establishing a radio link between the Arctic and the Antarctic using Collins equipment.

The gamble had paid off, for Byrd, for CBS, and for Collins. In as little time as it took an amateur radio operator to

The large 20B transmitter used by the Byrd expedition was designed primarily as a broadcast transmitter, although some amateur operators who wanted maximum power also used it.

put out his call, word of the Collins equipment success spread through the ham world.

The Collins radios used by Byrd employed new ideas which were later widely adopted in the radio field. These included: multiple pretuned radio frequency bays which allowed the operator to make frequency changes more quickly than previously possible, and unitized construction which gave the radios top-notch quality and reliability.

Another feature of the radios was a system called Class B modulation, which allowed large audio power from relatively small tubes. Collins Radio Company virtually pioneered the application of Class B modulation in low- and medium-powered transmitters.

The performance of the Collins equipment in transmitting voices from Antarctica produced a boom in orders for equipment among both amateur and commercial buyers worldwide.

Growth in the 1930s

The publicity and prestige resulting from the Byrd expedition sent the company on its way toward expansion. A company newsletter, called *Collins Signal,* was started in January, 1934. The work force was increased.

One of those who applied for work with the growing company was Milo Soukup.

"Jobs were scarce," Milo recalls, "we couldn't even get into the Civilian Conservation Corps, which was the government jobs program. Leo, my older brother, got on at Collins because of the influence of his friend, Ted Saxon, and I also wanted a job."

Because he was only 16, Milo wasn't immediately given a factory job, but Arthur's father arranged for Milo to work around the family home on Fairview Drive, doing work around the house and driving M. H.'s Cadillac. A year later, Soukup was put on the assembly crew. His job was to sand and varnish wooden spars used in radio cabinets.

Other contracts came in for diverse applications of radio equipment. Unusual requests seemed to be the usual at Collins Radio Company.

There was Father Hubbard, the glacier priest, who had his Collins communications gear adapted for dogsled travel in Arctic regions.

There was the Maharajah of Mysore, who in 1935 ordered a Collins transmitter to take with him on a tiger hunt in India. He purchased four receivers — one for each wife — so he could talk to them while on safari.

Firestone Tire and Rubber Co. purchased an early transmitter for use in Liberia, Africa. There was no port at the designated place of delivery, so Collins employees sealed the packed transmitter in a large horse-watering tank and instructed the shippers to float it ashore. At high tide, a freighter carried the tank as close to the shore as it could, then tossed it overboard. At low tide natives towed it ashore

Dr. James M. B. Hard with his portable transmitter, designed especially for travel.

with oxen. The radio replaced a former telegraph system because the natives had cut down the copper wire lines to create jewelry.

One of the best known customers in the ham community was Dr. James M. B. Hard of Mexico City. He chose Collins equipment in 1933 for his new installation, and had it specially designed for his needs. Dr. Hard spent weekends away from the city and wanted equipment he could take with him, so he commissioned Collins to design a special carrying case and distinctive equipment that would all easily fit into the trunk of his new Packard.

Also in those early days radio equipment was produced for a Harvard expedition to Russia to study an eclipse, and for noted explorer Sir Hubert Wilkins in his search for missing Russian fliers in the Arctic.

To further advertise the capabilities of the growing company, a team of Collins "representatives" traveled to the 1933 Chicago World's Fair. The team of representatives actually amounted to the entire work force, except for the office women. "We thought our equipment was the hit of the show," recalled Jiggs Ozburn, although he admitted belly dancer sensation Little Egypt also stirred some excitement at the fair.

As world markets grew, several men were hired as Collins representatives to foreign countries. M. H. Collins and William Houk worked on contracts in Mexico in 1934, and the next year Raymond Billings and Frank Goodrich also made visits to Mexico. Jamie Lopez of Bogota, Columbia, was made the company's South American representative.

Ozburn recalled that Arthur would sometimes come out to his ham shack and talk business via radio with Clair Miller in Mexico City.

Two complete mobile communication stations mounted in two trucks were assembled for the Spanish Government during the Spanish civil war in 1937. Roger Pierce recalled that Spain sent two representatives who couldn't speak English to Cedar Rapids to supervise the work, and none of the Collins employees could speak Spanish, but the equipment seemed to work in either language, Pierce said.

Many police departments around the country were beginning to use two-way radios, and by 1938, Collins had supplied equipment for police in Lodi, California; Connersville, Indiana; Urbana, Illinois; Huron, South Dakota; and Ottumwa and Cedar Rapids, Iowa.

The radio most of those police departments purchased was a model Collins introduced in September, 1935, called the 45A transmitter. It provided increased power and improved efficiency in a compact table-top unit. By December, sales to amateur and commercial users were running high, and Collins increased production to meet the unexpected number of sales.

Several new Collins transmitters for broadcast radio stations were also introduced in 1935, although many in the industry were convinced the product wouldn't work well enough to sell. A Tennessee radio station was the first to install a Collins transmitter using Class B modulation, which was a radical departure from the modulation system that was

23

The Cedar Rapids Police Department was one of the first to use two-way radios in squad cars. This 1935 photograph shows Henry Nemec, who later worked for Collins, using a 150B transmitter, similar to the one used by Admiral Byrd. Collins also built mobile equipment for police operations.

then the broadcast industry standard. The equipment proved that adopting the Class B modulation theory not only required smaller tubes and other smaller components — which meant less space, less power and less expense — but that the end product, the transmission itself, was of higher quality.

With all the orders coming in, the company needed more factory and office space. In 1935, the factory portion was moved to a storeroom at the corner of Seventh Street and First Avenue. In 1937, the factory rejoined the office department at the 2920 First Avenue address, but by then the operation was too large for the original building, so the production force of more than 80 persons was moved to a building behind the offices.

Total 1934 sales of $129,000 more than doubled in 1935, and increased to $391,000 by 1936.

With his growing reputation, Collins was able to attract highly skilled employees, many with extensive radio experience.

Robert Gates came to the company in 1935 and was made treasurer. Rose Hansen, the former secretary of the Collins Farms Company, became secretary.

L. E. Bessemer joined in 1935 and served as a principal development engineer. L. Morgan Craft brought with him a

Upper
Cedar Rapids Police squad cars displayed in front of city hall, 1935.

Lower
The Collins 45A transmitter.

broad background in physics and electronics, and was a guiding factor in the company's design and development policies. Walter Wirkler collaborated with Arthur Collins on new modulation designs.

A former associate of Lee De Forest also came to work for the Collins Radio Company. William Barkley had become general manager of De Forest Radio Co. and Wireless Specialty Co., one of the earliest manufacturers of radio equipment. It was Barkley who coined the phrase "The Father of Radio" to describe De Forest. Barkley joined Collins in 1935 as executive vice president and sales manager of the new Collins sales office in New York, and later became executive vice president of the company.

One of the sales negotiated by Barkley that elevated Collins Radio to the ranks of the large communication equipment companies was a substantial contract with the Union of South Africa concluded just before the United States entered World War II. This sale was more than the total sales of any year in the company's earlier history. Later, this radio equipment was to have an important part in the battles of the North African campaign.

The year 1935 also brought another sign of the company's growth. Time clocks were installed.

Above
A group of 100-watt lighthouse radiotelephone transmitters, LSR-319, built by Collins for the U.S. Department of Commerce, were lined up along the west wall of the building at Seventh Street and First Avenue, later occupied by Modern Laundry.

Left
Office group at the First Avenue building in 1934 included, left to right: Katherine Horsfall, Frances Power, Park Rinard, Irene Snyder, Faye (Jones) Dunn, Betty (Cocayne) Davis, Lucille (Eller) Dotson, and Marjorie (Black) James.

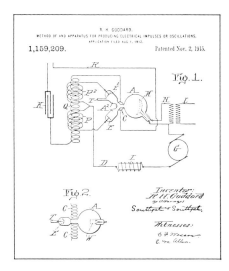

Upper
Goddard's original vacuum tube
patent.

Lower
Robert H. Goddard. Photo from the
Bettmann Archive, Inc.

Right
This collection of tubes represented
many of the types built by Collins
in the 1930s. The "Y-shaped" tube
in the top right corner was built as
an exhibit in the RCA patent litiga-
tion as a copy of Goddard's patent,
which was cited as prior art to the
De Forest oscillator patent.

Aided by a fellow scientist

During this pre-war period of growth, Collins Radio, along with other small and growing radio manufacturers, experienced difficulties in procuring components, especially vacuum tubes, from the major manufacturers.

Two of the largest companies, RCA and AT&T, made a significant move to squeeze out the small companies by claiming they had patent rights on vacuum tubes designed by De Forest and Dr. Edwin Howard Armstrong. RCA and AT&T had adopted the policy of not granting licenses for the manufacture of radio transmitters, and they sued Collins Radio Company.

Arthur Collins wasn't satisfied to sit back and watch his growing company be strangled, so he asked his patent attorney, John Brady of Washington, D.C., to make a search of the De Forest "file wrapper." After some research into the problem, Brady discovered that Robert Goddard, the famous rocket pioneer, had applied for and received a patent in 1915 on an oscillator tube that was an early form of the radio tube principle later employed by De Forest and Armstrong.

Collins appealed to Goddard to help Collins Radio beat RCA and AT&T in the legal action. In 1936, Arthur Collins traveled to Goddard's home at Roswell, New Mexico, where Goddard was engaged in rocket research and testing. The two scientists discussed the situation, and Goddard assured Collins he would consider his request for help.

While Goddard was considering Collins' appeal, RCA sent an emissary to Roswell to ask Goddard if his tube actually worked.

"Of course my tube works," Goddard replied testily to the

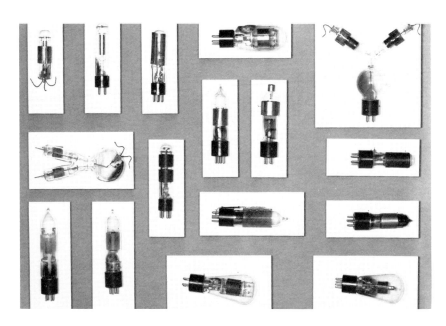

RCA representative.

His inventiveness insulted, Goddard became ardent in his support of Collins. Armed with the help of the renowned Dr. Goddard, Collins was able to get RCA and AT&T to modify their licensing policies and grant a patent license to Collins, and to many other companies.

"Dr. Goddard didn't ask a thing for himself," Collins later recalled for Goddard's biographer. He accepted only a modest consultant's fee, saying it would be enough to pay for another patent.

Because of Goddard's assistance, Collins Radio Company was able to continue manufacturing and selling its radio equipment.

Something called the Autotune®

Growth of the company in the 1930s brought with it a broadening product line.

But from the beginning it was Collins policy to manufacture and sell only equipment of its own design and development. That policy was continued as the product lines expanded, leading Collins to become a major contributor to progress in the industry.

Collins Radio Company found that its radios, originally designed for the amateur radio market, were being applied in commercial and government situations as well.

Starting in 1934, Collins produced a 600-watt transmitter specifically designed for commercial radio. A line of broadcast transmitters also was introduced, starting in 1933 with a shortwave transmitter that was followed by a conventional 250-watt broadcast transmitter in 1934.

The first airborne application of a Collins radio came in 1934 when the Goodyear Tire Company's 12th commercial blimp, the Enterprise, was launched with a Collins transmitter on board. Large and heavy by today's standards, the transmitter provided effective communication for the airship crew stationed at Hoover Field in Washington, D.C.

Sales in the blimp market were sparse compared with the potential sales of radio for airplanes, which were quickly coming of age as commercial vehicles.

A major problem airline operators faced in the early 1930s was the need to use a number of different transmitting frequencies within short periods of time. Different frequencies had to be used for plane-to-plane, plane-to-ground, and airport control tower communication. Changes in frequency were needed at night when changing atmospheric conditions made communications over a particular channel impossible.

Above
A Collins transmitter was installed in the Enterprise *in 1934, making it the first known airborne application of a Collins radio.*

Right
The Goodyear blimp Enterprise *as it appeared in 1935.*

But it took valuable time to re-tune a transmitter from one channel to another. A pilot coming into a field low on fuel couldn't waste time twiddling dials. Nor could he wait for a ground operator to switch frequencies.

The company and its 26-year-old boss tackled the problem, and hit upon an idea that was to have a major impact on the future of the company and an effect on the outcome of a world war.

For several years, Arthur Collins and his engineers studied the problem and worked on solutions for rapid radio band switching and tuning.

Then the solution hit.

Significantly enough, the solution occurred to Collins while he was on a commercial airline flight from Mexico City in 1935. Basically, the idea was a simple one — combine mechanical engineering principles with those of electronics. The theory was to link all of the tuning controls of a transmitter into one common dialing system. The Autotune® was born.

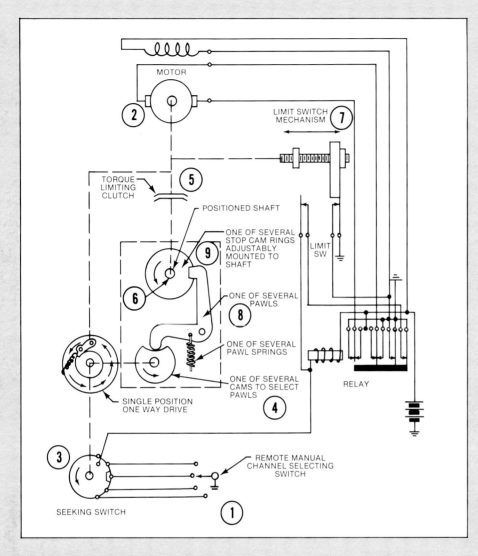

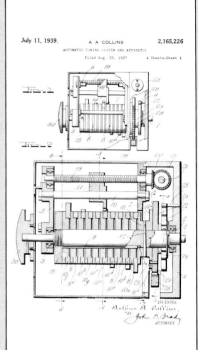

To select a frequency using the Autotune, the radio operator simply dialed a frequency on the channel selecting switch (1). An electric circuit then caused the motor (2) to start turning the mechanism in the direction of the arrows, and by means of ratchets drove the seeking switch (3) and cam drum (4). The clutch (5) turned the positioned shaft (6) toward the home or reference end of its travel. The positioned shaft was directly connected to the tuning mechanism of whatever radio was being tuned. The shaft came to rest against the home stop. The clutch then slipped, allowing the motor to continue running. The limit switch (7) operated, allowing the motor to reverse as soon as the seeking switch found the selected position, and released the relay reversing the motor. The cam drum and

the seeking switch remained stationary. The controls were then set and the proper pawl (8) was in position. The shaft turned until the selected pawl engaged its corresponding stop ring (9) on the shaft. The positioning was then complete. The clutch slipped as the motor continued to run. The other limit switch operated and stopped the motor, ending the cycle.

For each preset frequency, a different pawl-stop ring-cam combination was used. They were located side by side on the same shafts, with spacers between them. Usually ten preset frequencies were possible. An airborne radio typically required five Autotunes driven by a common motor. Each Autotune was connected to a tuning device that required re-positioning for a frequency change.

Upper
The patent drawing for an advanced form of the Autotune showed the precision machining required to manufacture the device.

Lower
A typical Autotune was the 96J. Four of these were connected to a larger 96K Autotune head to allow the pilot to select 100 frequencies on the Collins 17H radio.

Upper
Braniff Airways was the first airline to install Collins Autotune equipment for its fleet of DC-3s and other aircraft.

Lower
The first airborne transmitter to use the Autotune was the Collins 17D, manufactured for Braniff.

With the Autotune, switching from one band to another became as quick and easy as pushing a button.

The Autotune made it possible for pilots to easily control ten quick-shift channels at a time when airplane cockpits were becoming more and more complicated.

The 1937 edition of *Aero Digest* hailed the Autotune as "a major advance in aircraft radio design and construction," and the airlines were quick to see the benefits.

The United Fruit Company was the first customer, buying a six-circuit Autotune for its Central American ground stations.

Even though the Federal Radio Commission had a rule limiting aircraft radio transmitters to 50 watts, Collins developed a 100-watt transmitter which used the Autotune and sold it to Braniff Airways. Pink violation slips piled on Braniff's desk, but after a lengthy hassle, the government finally permitted Braniff and other carriers to raise their power. By 1937, Braniff became the first airline to equip its entire fleet with Collins Radio equipment. American Airlines also saw the importance of the invention, and became a major customer for Collins Autotune radios.

With the Autotune, Collins Radio Company entered the world of aviation.

The production departments of the company returned to the 2920 First Avenue location in 1937. Instead of occupying the basement of the three-story building (top of photo) as they previously did, most factory operations took place in the larger one-story building immediately behind. This view looks east, with First Avenue in the background.

A 1938 publicity photograph taken at one of the First Avenue buildings showed 26 men working on the assembly line. In reality, employees were brought in from other work areas to make the assembly area appear larger than it was at that time, according to Milo Soukup. Those identified, outside row: Paul Hauser, Walker Whitmore, Kenny Vaughn, Harry Rogers, Dick Gintert, Buck Holsinger, Les Bessemer, Dale McCoy, unidentified, Archie Torson. Second row: Bob Davis, Ray Stoner, Soukup, Al Keyes; Third row: Tom McGregor, Bill Popek, Bruce Miller, Del Zarub, Chuck Hatfield, Claude Hoppe, Leonard Braun, Elmer Koehn; Fourth row: Charlie Gould, Henry Dmitruk, Don Tubbesing, and Arlo Goodyear.

Far Left
Cabling operation

Near Left
Spot welding

Opposite Page
Turret lathe

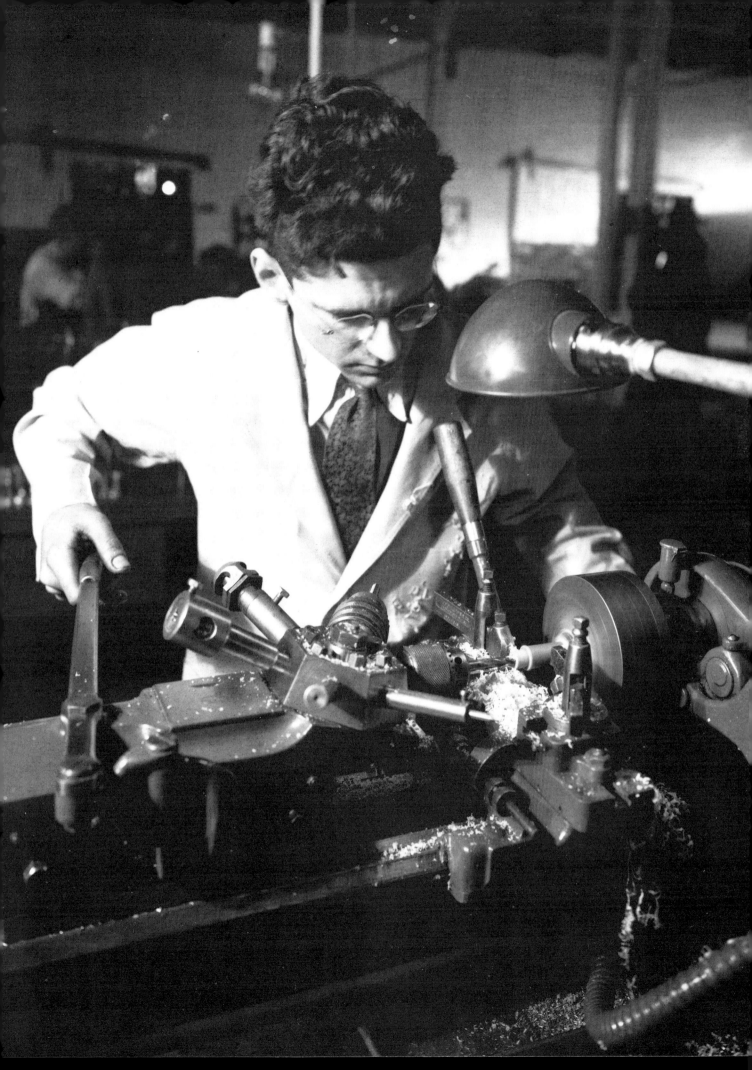

Above
Metal department

Right
Robert Miller with a group of 7C amplifiers

Lower Left
Panel engraving

Lower Right
Paint room

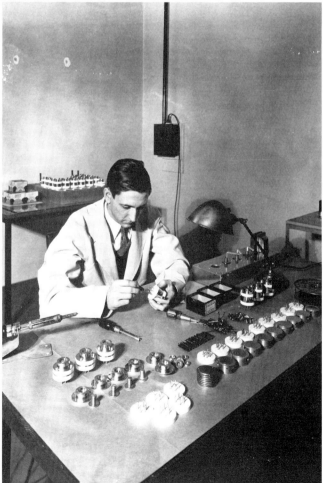

Upper
Transmitter assembly area

Lower
At first, shipping was handled by an outside firm, but by 1937 the company had its own department for packing and shipping.

Left
Crystal holder department

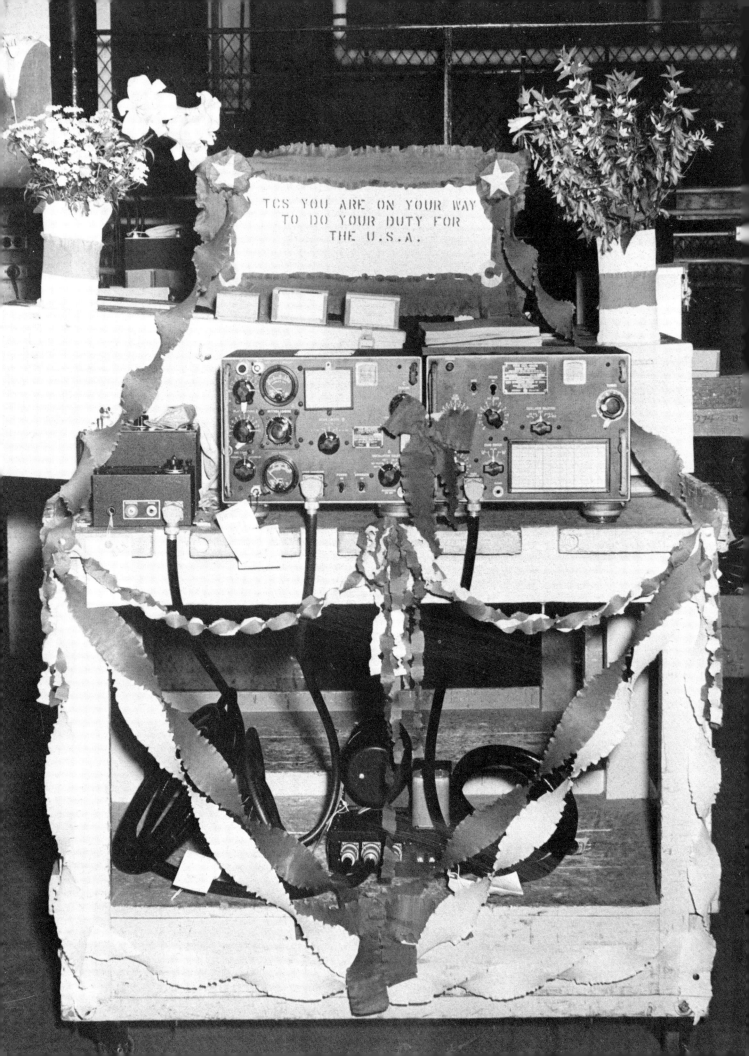

3

The war years

In 1939, the Nazi armies of Hitler invaded Poland. Despite the best attempts of American leaders to stay neutral in the European war, the Roosevelt administration was grimly aware that the United States was likely to be drawn into the battle, and that it needed to build military strength to effectively help its European friends.

The U.S. Navy was given the go-ahead to build a fleet second to none. Newly developed vessels — destroyers escorts, PCEs, flat-bottomed, shovel-nosed landing craft and baby carriers — slid down the ways and splashed into bays and launching areas. At the same time the Navy's air arm developed and expanded.

With a two-ocean navy and air arm underway, instant and reliable communication became a vital factor if this burgeoning fleet was to be welded into a trim fighting force. A system of communications that had been adequate for the needs of a small peacetime navy with experienced radio operators became clogged to the point of strangulation with the increase in operational traffic of a fleet preparing for war.

During this period Collins Radio Company, still less than

Opposite Page
The rugged little TCS was one of the radios mass-produced by Collins during World War II. More than 35,000 were built for use in small vessels and land vehicles. When the last TCS came off the production line, an informal ceremony marked the occasion. Photo courtesy Kenneth Everhart.

Right
The Collins AN/ART-13 transmitter was credited with saving the lives of many allied pilots during World War II.

ten years old, joined the Navy.

In the early spring of 1940, a board of naval air officers put prototype transmitters of three companies through a series of rigorous tests. Two of the transmitters were developed and introduced by companies long established and well-known in the field of electronics. The third transmitter — submitted by Collins Radio Company of Cedar Rapids, Iowa, "won the competition overwhelmingly," according to one of the officers conducting the tests. For the fleet air arm, the Collins AN/ART-13 offered a completely new field of flexibility. This was the first remote-controlled transmitter in naval aviation, and was the first time that radio equipment could be conveniently "pilot operated," permitting the remaining crew members to be at other action stations. This situation also saved enormous training load for the Navy, as one officer pointed out, since it did not require a radioman to be aloft on smaller aircraft.

While other air-to-ground voice communication equipment of the period offered two- and three-frequency channels, the newly-developed Collins radio gave pilots nearly instantaneous selection of any one of ten frequencies.

A key design factor in this big step forward in naval air communications was the Collins Autotune, which permitted almost instant changing of frequencies.

The autotuned AN/ART-13 became the flagship of Collins Radio's efforts during the war. Collins produced 26,000 of

The Collins ART-13 transmitter flew aboard every B-29 Superfortress during World War II. Boeing photo.

Upper
The autotuned ART-13 was installed on fighter airplanes, such as the F4U Corsair. Official U.S. Navy photograph.

Lower
Many small U.S. Navy vessels such as PT boats were equipped with the Collins TCS radio during World War II. Photo from the Bettmann Archive, Inc.

Right
The ART-13 transmitter and antenna coupler were located on the radio operator's left in this view of a B-29 radio room.

the 100-watt airborne transmitters; and with other companies following Collins' designs and specifications, more than 90,000 were supplied not only to the U.S. Navy but to all of the nation's armed forces, plus those of the British.

A high ranking naval officer credited the ART-13 for literally saving the lives of American pilots in World War II. Just after Pearl Harbor, America's carrier-based planes were equipped with transmitters which had only four pre-tuned frequencies available. Each time an American Navy pilot took off in the first days of the war he was flying into a stacked deck, because Japanese intelligence was well aware of these four fixed frequencies. The enemy either jammed Navy transmissions or forced the carrier to keep radio silence on the four frequencies to avoid giving away its location.

Installed in Navy planes soon after the war began, Collins Autotune transmitters provided a turning point in naval flight operations. The transmitters offered any combination of ten automatically tuned frequencies. In 15 seconds a pilot could select any of the frequencies, and before each operation the ten frequencies could be changed, making it almost impossible for the enemy to monitor or jam American transmissions.

Developed during the same period was a compact combination transmitter-receiver designed for use aboard small vessels and land vehicles. Designated the TCS, this rugged little set was produced in quantities exceeding 35,000. It saw action in all theaters of the war — from PT boats skipping across waters of the Pacific to jeeps motoring along the autobahns of Germany.

A small Collins-built radio transmitter, buried deep in one of the tunnels of Fort Mills on Corregidor Island in Manila Bay, was the United States' only contact with its own and allied forces in the Pacific during the tragic early days of the war with Japan.

Several months before the Japanese attack on Pearl Harbor, the commander-in-chief of the Asiatic fleet, Admiral Thomas C. Hart, directed the installation of an emergency Navy radio station in one of the tunnels of Fort Mills. This was in anticipation of probable destruction of all normal military communications facilities in the very early stages of the war, foresight that later proved to be correct in every detail.

The very first day of the battle for Manila saw all normal communication installations of the Army and Navy completely wiped out. Space, power and antenna limitations imposed by the concrete-lined tunnels on Corregidor restricted emergency station transmitters to relatively small and low-powered apparatus, including one shiny new Collins radio called a TCC.

As General Douglas MacArthur made his famous "I shall return" statement before evacuating the island, allied forces retreated into the tunnels of Fort Mills in a final attempt to ward off the advancing Japanese forces.

After considerable experimenting, the remaining radiomen rigged an antenna with feeders that ran more than 100 feet before leaving the tunnel and turning down the hillside.

"Any radioman, viewing our weird installation, would have been convinced that we would be fortunate to get a signal across Manila Bay. Such, however, was not the case. The antenna system worked perfectly, even during bombing and bombardments when the antenna would be down or cut; our signal was not interrupted and we continued to put a strength five signal into Honolulu, many thousands of miles away," Lt. Comdr. C. A. Walruff later wrote:

"The most amazing part of the whole story is that the Collins TCC, which we all considered as very pretty in its nice enamel cabinet, very fancy with its telephone dial frequency shifting system, but probably not very rugged, turned out to be the most successful of all the apparatus available in the Far East. After our main radio station at Cavite was destroyed, the tunnel station on Corregidor took over all circuits, and the TCC was found to be the only transmitter which would work Honolulu. From that day on, until many hours *after* Corregidor had actually surrendered, every word that reached the United States from China, the Philippines, Singapore, Java and from our Asiatic Fleet was poured into Honolulu by the little Collins TCC (one-kilowatt) transmitter, keyed by high speed automatic equipment.

"The Collins transmitter maintained overseas communications for the Commander-in-Chief of the American, British and Dutch Naval forces and for the Army, as well as occasionally participating in the broadcast schedules for our submarine forces, which were even then causing tremendous losses for the Japs.

"It was not until after Java had fallen, and our forces had retreated to southwest Australia, that this tremendous responsibility was lifted from the brightly enameled frame of the very reliable, high-performance Collins TCC."

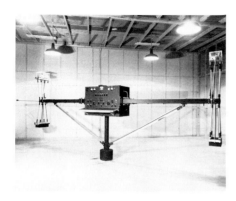

Another Collins contribution during the war was a high frequency direction finder. A rotating beam-mounted loop antenna system, it played a key role in locating enemy submarines, particularly in the Atlantic. Collins tested this equipment in a two-story wooden blockhouse building nicknamed Fort Dearborn. At the time, the project was so secret that the doors of the assembly area were kept locked and admittance was granted to only a few employees who had been thoroughly investigated by the FBI. The direction finder was developed by engineers Gilbert Oberweiser, Willard Heath and Dale McCoy. Over a hundred of the units were made at Collins for the Navy.

Collins also built combination transmitters and receivers for mobile use during the war, and its large and powerful transmitters were used at Navy shore stations, air bases and army headquarters in all theaters of operation. It was via Collins transmitters aboard the U.S.S. Missouri in Tokyo Bay that the V-J Day surrender ceremonies were heard throughout the world.

Tremendous growth

When Collins Radio Company received the first orders for military radios in 1940, total employment was approximately 150. Many of the production workers were ham radio operators who had been attracted by the reputation of Collins equipment.

Company leaders realized that new government orders meant Collins would have to undertake a large expansion program to meet the requirements of the contracts.

The company also took a hard look at its long-term prospects, realizing that the electronics industry was about to branch into many new fields. In 1941, chief engineer Morgan Craft began a selective search for top young engineers who could lay a foundation for future growth. Of the approximately 15 who were hired, many made significant contributions to Collins Radio, and later, other firms.

Included in the Collins "Class of '41" were William Anderson, Robert Cox, Melvin Doelz, Mike Fitzgerald, Richard May, John Nyquist, Ernie Pappenfus, Ross Pyle, John Sherwood and others.

On Nov. 4, 1940, the articles of incorporation were amended to increase the authorized capital stock from 250 shares to 1,000 shares of common stock. To provide funds to undertake expansion plans, the company took a mortgage of $100,000 on its real and personal property.

In the fall of 1940, construction of a new 52,000-square-foot plant started on a 26-acre tract between 32nd and 35th

Above
Main Plant, January 1941.

Streets N.E. in Cedar Rapids. The area was formerly a swampy pasture on the edge of town. Residential neighborhoods extended northward to about 29th Street at the time of the initial construction.

By January, 1941, many of the company's departments had moved out of the facilities at 2920 First Avenue and into the new 35th Street plant. Six months later a second construction project — an addition to the plant on the south and east sides which would more than double the size of the building — was announced. The $500,000 structure was built under an emergency plant facilities contract, with the U.S. government to reimburse Collins for the cost of the addition.

The last pieces of furniture for the new engineering areas and machinery for the factory area were being moved into place as word of the Japanese attack on Pearl Harbor reached the mainland.

The growth of Collins Radio suddenly began to mushroom. There was a war on, and the patriotic call went out across the country. Those who couldn't serve in the armed forces were expected to contribute at home, and for many that meant work in a war plant. Because of the radios built for all branches of the military, Collins became the largest war plant in Cedar Rapids. Amateur and commercial product lines were shut down, and all efforts were channeled into military equipment. Men who never intended to be supervisors found themselves heading large groups of workers. They had to learn by trial and error because there were no management courses in the early months of the war.

On December 22, 1941, the production requirements forced the company to cancel all leaves of absence during the holiday season. Operation on Christmas Day was "restricted" but not shut down completely for both office and factory workers.

More workers were hired in attempts to keep up with the increasing production quotas of the military, and vacations were cancelled.

Out of necessity, the company developed written pro-

cedures to assure uniformity for all aspects of production. There simply weren't enough instructors to go around to train new people by word-of-mouth, as had been the pre-war practice.

In February, 1942, the first women production workers were hired at Collins. A memo dated January 22, 1942 attempted to assure the male workers: "There will be no replacement of present male employees by women." Women of all ages helped fabricate and assemble radio equipment.

At first the women were stationed in a special area separate from the men — "penned up," as one employee recalls, "so they wouldn't be harassed by those nasty men." When management felt women and men could work side by side,

ART-13 drill press section, April 1944. The health message on the poster above the woman at left states "Coughs and sneezes spread diseases, please the Germans, and Japaneses!"

restrictions on working areas for women were lifted. By the time the war production reached its peak in 1944, more than half the Collins assembly workers were women. To encourage more to apply, a short shift practice was adopted so housewives could work from 6:30 p.m. to 10:30 p.m.

Two women were hired as matrons for the women factory workers. Isabell Duncan and Luella Chapman assisted the women at the plant and handed out smocks for them to wear over their clothes.

Milo Soukup, a foreman during the war, recalled one morning when five girls from the Amana Colonies (a disbanded German ethnic society near Cedar Rapids) reported for work in his department. "I never saw five girls that worked as hard. We always asked the personnel office if

Assembly area for the TCS radio. This view was taken from the north end of Main Plant in October, 1944.

they had any more from the Amanas.

"It wasn't unusual for 18 new employees to be brought into a department twice a week," said Soukup. "We were told to put them to work. We were glad to have them, because other industries were also competing for people. We seemed to get good quality workers because they were screened by the personnel department."

In January, 1942, Madge Taylor (Nabholtz) and Ruby MacArthur (Pyle) were hired as the first registered nurses at the company. A third nurse, Clela Dugan, was hired later that year.

Each day more workers were brought in from the surrounding area and put to work, some commuting as far as 60 miles one way. In the early days of tire and gasoline rationing, the personnel office set up a transportation department to make sure war plant employees received their allocations to get to work. The company's transportation director, Lucille Horner, arranged car pool rides for 1,644 persons in 393 vehicles. The average number of passengers per car was 4.2, the highest occupancy rate in the state.

The first copies of a new company publication, *Collins Column* were mailed in May, 1943. The newsletter, edited by Marian Kimball, was designed to be a morale booster for employees serving in the military.

A new cafeteria was constructed south of the 35th Street building, which by then had come to be called the Main Plant. Opened on Sept. 6, 1944, the cafeteria had seating capacity for 488 persons. An outside company managed the cafeteria.

Collins also worked closely with Cedar Rapids City Lines bus company to schedule routes to the many Collins Radio plants. *(See accompanying story.)*

The physical separation of the departments made an elaborate telephone system necessary. Three complete exchanges were installed, each large enough to serve an average-size Iowa town.

Despite the hardships of rationing and long work days, morale during the war was excellent.

"The workers all felt they were part of the war effort," Soukup said. "There was no dissension, no complaints. It was a time of nice cooperative effort. It was all **our** job, not the other guy's problem."

Soukup pointed out, however, that the average person on the line during World War II probably didn't understand everything about the products he or she was building.

"One person was asked by a plant visitor what she was working on. She replied that she couldn't tell because it was

Upper

Collins employees who shared the ride to work during the war had the highest per-vehicle occupancy rate in the state of Iowa. One of the more crowded vehicles was a panel truck driven by Tom Holland of Independence. Pictured from left: Holland; Marjorie Holloway, Ruth Willer, Floyd Holloway, Ira Wheeler, Keith Kennedy, Homer Kennedy, Leo Rogers, Don Holloway and Howard Weigand, all of Center Point; LaMar Guernsey of Urbana; and Sherman Hovey, Harley Dingsley, Walter Scott and Guy Beatty of Independence.

Middle

The new employee cafeteria near the Main Plant. September 1944.

Lower

Interior of the new cafeteria. According to the menu posted on the wall, the plate lunch of pot roast and noodles, mashed potatoes or beets, plus bread and butter cost a total of 40 cents.

a 'military secret.' Actually it wasn't a military secret, but our attitude was that we had a job to do and we did it. What the product did, well, that was up to the engineers."

The dedication to the war effort was recognized by the military when Collins Radio Company was awarded the coveted Army-Navy "E" emblem. On Sept. 19, 1942, 4,000 persons gathered on the front lawn of Main Plant to watch William Willson and Alice Rinderknecht accept the pennant on behalf of Collins Radio employees from Brig. Gen. Charles Grahl, state director for selective services. Standing in a special reserved section facing the platform were family members and the 1,200 employees of Collins Radio.

Upper
To celebrate meeting the December, 1943 quota in the ART-13 assembly area, employees decorated the 1,500th radio with ribbons. Elmer Koehn, superintendent of the department, wore a ribbon on his head for the photograph. Standing behind the "1500" sign is Arthur Collins, and to Collins' left is J. W. "Slim" Dayhoff, production superintendent.

Lower
The Collins Radio accounting department, December 31, 1943.

49

The war years

"Our job is to provide our full share of the lightning-fast radio couriers which will carry vital dispatches, commands, and reports to and from the growing thousands of ships and airplanes fighting a tremendous war extending over the entire world," Arthur Collins said in a speech to the crowd. "To do this job each one of us must increase his skill, improve his workmanship, speed his hands, and sharpen his wits. We must not only do the work at hand, but also prepare ourselves for many new problems to come."

Because of continued improvements in production, the company's "E" emblem award was renewed five times.

Employment numbers grew to keep pace with rising quotas, until a wartime peak of 3,332 was reached on July 15, 1945. As the summer progressed, it became apparent that the Allies would be victorious. Victory in Europe was fol-

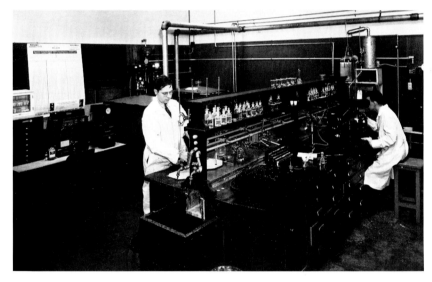

Upper
Phil Evans and John Grahm in the chemical laboratory. The lab, a group of test personnel, and assembly lines were located in the basement of the Shrine Temple. April 1944.

Lower
Payroll department at the Third Street building, 1945.

During the height of wartime production at Collins Radio Company, production lines swelled with new employees. In line with the growing national labor movement, union organizing began at the plant.

In February, 1943, the company signed an agreement with an organization called the Collins Radio Employees Association (CREA). The contract included provisions for treatment of grievances, working conditions, negotiations, seniority rights and privileges, vacation policy and a bracket pay system.

But in May of that year the American Federation of Labor (AFL) and the Congress of Industrial Organizations (CIO) filed separate complaints, charging that the CREA was not a legal collective bargaining unit.

The National Labor Relations Board agreed. The NLRB ruled that because of the rapid expansion of the company during the previous two years, many organizers of the CREA had been made supervisors at the time of the contract. Therefore the CREA was ruled to be a "company-dominated" union, and NLRB recognition was withdrawn.

An election was held August 3, 1943, for production and maintenance employees to choose a new collective bargaining unit.

The results: International Brotherhood of Electrical Workers (affiliated with the AFL), 1,095; Radio Union, 717; Collins Radio Union, 57; and "no union" votes, 92.

The first officers elected for Local 1362 of the I.B.E.W. were, Bernard Rankin, president; John Lyons, vice president; Abe Mashman, first inspector; Lois Wallace, recording secretary; Edwin Pitts, treasurer; Frank Ross, financial secretary; Joe Buresch, foreman; and John Mitch, second inspector.

The first contract was negotiated October 11, 1943. The agreement raised the base wage to 57 cents and the maximum to $1.65 per hour, from the previous marks of 45 cents and $1.20, respectively. Equal pay was established for men and women doing the same job.

A steward system was provided to handle grievances, and holiday and vacation benefits were included in the contract.

In 1947, the AFL and the CIO joined to form a new national organization, the AFL-CIO.

A pension plan for bargaining units employees was negotiated in 1949.

Local 1362 grew from 68 members to 448 by 1948, and reached a peak of 6,500 in 1967.

In October, 1967, a labor dispute, primarily over wages, caused a strike by Local 1362 which lasted 16 days. In May, 1976, another strike, principally over cost-of-living increases, lasted 29 days.

Past Local 1362 presidents: Bernie Rankin, Abe Mashman, Joe Frycek, Wayne Disterhoff, Louis Schlatterback, W. D. Neff, Toby Arnold, Jerry Beer, Pete Jurgim, Craig Hoepner and Pat Marshall (present). Past business managers: John Lyon, Paul Anderson, Al Meier, John Hunter, Doug Heiden, Gary Heald, and Norm Sterzenbach (present).

Two other unions also represent workers at the Collins Divisions in Cedar Rapids.

Teamsters Local No. 238, a general local union with about 4,000 members, first represented employees in the data processing group in 1964. At that time there were 164 employees in the unit. Some of the early members were Vern Johnson, Ella Holland, Gene Poppe, George Abodeely, Jobie Atwater, and Carl Garrels. During the late 1960s Collins tape librarians and distribution clerks voted to become part of the unit. In 1974, the data conversion operators also joined.

The charter organizing a security guard union was signed January 12, 1945. The International Brotherhood of Electrical Workers Local 1429 elected Paul Walshire as its first president. Succeeding presidents were: Marvin Kuba, Harry B. Hall, Everett Freeman, Don Crowley, Robert Schoon, Al Herman, and Carolyn Duffy.

lowed by victory over Japan, and Collins employees celebrated.

When all was tallied, wartime contracts at Collins totaled $110 million, including $46.5 million in fiscal year 1943-44. But because of tight government pricing controls, the profit margin for the work was relatively small — a scant 0.4 percent.

The dollar figures only partially indicate the significance of the company's wartime achievement. Since all the products were of its own design and development, Collins assisted several other companies in the production of Collins-designed military equipment during late stages of the war.

There was also the ultimate human contribution made by four Collins employees in the armed forces who were killed in action during the war.

Pvt. Denver Baxter: October 9, 1943.

Capt. Patrick Casey: March 5, 1944.

Lt. Melvin Forey: June 8, 1944.

Cpl. Leonard Modracek: June 14, 1944.

The men's names were given special positions on a large plaque, which hung at the Main Plant, listing all Collins employees who served in the armed forces during the war.

Another loss felt by the company was the death of M. H. Collins, vice president, in April, 1943, at the age of 64.

Upper
Packed transmitters awaiting shipment to the Navy, May 1944.

Lower
An honor roll, which listed the names of Collins employees who served in the armed forces during the war, was placed near the east entrance at the Main Plant. Standing next to the plaque is Tim O'Brien, chief fire guard for Collins.

By 1943, Collins had leased nearly every available building in Cedar Rapids. The government required many of the businesses which owned the buildings to cut back activities if they were not involved in war production. At one point, Collins had departments in 23 leased buildings.

Some of the buildings had unique characteristics which had a lasting impression on the people who worked there. The large Shrine Temple, for example, housed the Autotune assembly in its basement and a roller skating rink on the first floor. Mary Henningson said she clearly remembers how the music of the roller rink above the assembly area filled the building as the night shift worked to meet quotas.

Upper
The Shrine Temple, at the corner of A Avenue and 6th Street N.E., was wartime home for the chemistry lab, test equipment design and assembly, and Autotune assembly. The building was also used as a National Guard armory.

Lower
Calder's Van and Storage building on A Avenue was used as a warehouse.

Upper
The Midland building was the location of sheet metal and finishing departments for Collins Radio.

Middle
The Smulekoff building housed Collins' spare parts department.

Lower
The Chandler Company buildings were used as warehouses.

Upper
Assembly area in the Shrine
Temple. April 1944.

Lower
Receiving and inspection
departments were housed in
the Wagner building.

4

Post-war restructuring

The end of the war brought drastic changes to Collins Radio Company.

During the previous four years the company had only one customer — Uncle Sam. With the war over, military contracts were cancelled or reduced. Of the original $47 million in orders on the company's books on July 31, 1945, $15 million remained after contract terminations and reductions. The remaining backlog represented advanced design programs requested by the military.

War contracts were terminated, and that meant physical conversion of the company's plant facilities for peacetime operation, accompanied by large-scale cutbacks in the work force. The company needed time to adjust to manufacture new product lines, and employees had to retrain.

Among the other war plants in Cedar Rapids, not all were as critically affected by the government contract cancellations. An August 17, 1945, *Cedar Rapids Gazette* story summarized the condition of local industries. At Century Engineering, two-thirds of the government contracts were cancelled. Cherry-Burrell quickly converted to peacetime production, and advertised for machinists and sheet metal workers. Quaker Oats continued to supply military provisions, but was anxious to resume its civilian business. At the Wilson and Company packing plant, no drop in employment occurred because the demand for meat increased after the war. Demand for highway construction equipment kept Iowa Manufacturing and Iowa Steel employment levels high. Similar stories were told for Link-Belt Speeder, Turner Company, National Oats, Penick and Ford, Freuhauf Trailer, and LaPlant-Choate. Employment levels at most of Cedar Rapids' factories remained high, primarily due to the nature of their businesses, and also because most had been able to continue producing and selling commercial goods during the war.

At Collins, however, the story was different. Production had been completely dedicated to the armed forces.

In August, 1945, Collins Radio announced a temporary five-day layoff of all production departments as management struggled to determine future employment needs. All leases

The Collins hangar with a Twin Beech 18 in 1946.

for space no longer necessary for operations were terminated.

One week later Robert Gates, company vice president, announced that within 30 days 2,000 employees would return to work, with the remaining 1,000 to be laid off for an extended length of time. Most of those laid off were women production line workers.

A survey made one year later showed that 79 percent of the women who had worked on the production lines at Collins had either quit voluntarily to resume pre-war lifestyles, or were laid off.

In June, 1945, a testing program was initiated for personnel. Prior to that the method used to fill a vacancy or new position was to select the person with seniority considered to be qualified for the job. This resulted in a certain percentage of persons (an estimated one-third) being placed in positions for which they were not qualified. Three types of tests were used to measure an employee's qualifications: 1. aptitude tests, 2. achievement or performance tests, and 3. dexterity tests. The tests were established in cooperation with the union, using input from the officers and stewards.

The biggest single factor affecting the profit picture at Collins was the cost of developing and tooling new products. Because the company had no commercial products ready for sale at the end of the war, the development and retooling costs were exceedingly high in relation to income. The years 1946 through 1948 showed net losses in earnings for the company.

The huge retooling effort undertaken by Collins Radio was

A group of veterans who returned to Collins posed beside the Main Plant.

On the morning of November 15, 1945, Arthur Collins, Frank Davis and Roy Olson were in conference. Collins had returned from a meeting at the Beech Aircraft Corporation at Wichita, Kansas, and had brought back with him an idea plus some sketches.

In the sudden hush of business following World War II, his company needed a commercial product to generate sales. At the same time the aviation industry was expecting a boom in private flying and needed a new, compact voice transmitter.

A survey of the possibilities indicated that a compact, straightforward design could be built with components that the company had on hand. Ten minutes later the project was assigned, carrying an "A.A.C." (Arthur A. Collins) priority in the model shop and production departments. Rough sketches were used in lieu of drawings, and chassis construction utilized paper templates, with the layout drawn on the paper. Parts were arranged on the chassis and holes drilled on the spot.

Ten days after its inception, the model and a remote control box were complete and tested. The 17E-2 was ready for installation in a twin-engine or large single-engine airplane.

During the next week, inquiries for the transmitter by those who saw the model indicated the immediate need for the 17E-2. The first production run was set at 200 units.

The technical ability, skill and experience demonstrated by the short turnaround time reinforced the slogan of the day, "If it can't be done, Collins will do it."

Roy Olson, Frank Davis and Arthur Collins check plans for a new aviation radio.

also reflected in employment and facilities. The Los Angeles sales office, established in 1946, was expanded and moved to Burbank, California, in 1949. Research and limited production facilities were added, and the Burbank facility became the Western Division of Collin Radio Company.

New personnel at Collins included some of the leading scientists in the fields of broadcast radio, radar, radio navigation, microwave communication, and aviation.

Marketing was given increased emphasis during the restructuring phase. A new marketing division was organized to cover all potential markets for the present and new products. W. J. Barkley, executive vice president, was a major contributor to the reorganization plans, along with Craft and Cox. Vice President Robert Gates was placed in charge of the procurement and marketing division. An export division was also formed in 1946, with Robert Parsons as manager.

To finance the development, the company in November, 1944, augmented its working capital by issuing public stock for the first time. Collins Radio Company sold 140,000 shares of common stock and 20,000 shares of preferred stock. The remaining 170,116 outstanding shares of common stock were retained by Collins family members and other managers. The sales added approximately $3 million to the company coffers.

By 1949, the new development efforts were paying off.

The company displayed its wares at the 1946 Iowa State Fair. At left is a TDO transmitter. Behind it is an oversized wooden model Autotune (on the table). Behind George Price are microwave antennas, a microwave receiver and transmitter, test equipment, and two display boards with microwave tubes and "plumbing."

COLLINS RADIO CO. DISPLAY
IOWA STATE FAIR
DES MOINES, IOWA
AUGUST 22-29, 1946

Collins was producing specialized electronic equipment and was shaping for a future larger and much more complicated than its past. Two markets in particular were to form the basis for the post-war growth of the company in the late 1940s and early 1950s: ultra-high frequency radios for the military; and commercial aviation electronics.

Military radio

During World War II the hundreds of channels required in joint operations of all types of ship, shore and aircraft units in military emergencies overcrowded the commonly-used frequencies. With commercial airlines already committed to the very high frequency (VHF) band, the Defense Department decided to vacate VHF after the war and move military short range communications into the practically unexplored ultra high frequency (UHF) band. Besides availability of channel space, the UHF region was free of static and largely free of man-made interference. The military could count on reliable UHF communication within the "line of sight" transmission range regardless of weather conditions.

The U.S. Navy, at the close of the war, sponsored development of a UHF airborne radio, and Western Electric Company developed an experimental model for the Navy to evaluate.

At the same time, the Army Air Corps was evaluating its own new UHF radio developed by the Bendix Corporation.

Collins Radio Company was also working on UHF development models in the late 1940s in an attempt to catch up with the advantageous positions held by Western Electric and Bendix with their respective branches of the armed forces. At stake were government contracts worth millions of dollars.

When the evaluation periods for the new UHF radios were completed, the Navy recommended that a Collins-designed UHF radio be chosen as the Navy standard, but the Army still favored its own development model.

In the final analysis, it was a new doctrine adopted by President Harry Truman which affected the outcome of the contract decisions. The experiences of World War II revealed weaknesses because of competition and lack of coordination between branches of the military. Truman proposed the creation of a separate air force and a single cabinet officer in charge of defense. The idea was opposed by the Army and Navy, but in June, 1947, a unified National Military Establishment was created. As part of that unification effort, the new Department of Defense required that a standard design would be used for the new UHF airborne radios for all military branches.

Sealed bids were taken for the initial order of 4,000 radios for the Navy, and Collins won the $7 million contract on the basis of both quality and cost. Because of the unification policy, the defense department also awarded the Air Force contract to Collins.

Linear-tuned circuits developed by Collins in 1944 had an extraordinary effect on communications equipment, and the new UHF radios were among the first to employ them. These circuits, coupled with the Autopositioner®, another Collins development related to the Autotune, made complete electrical remote tuning a reality. A radio operator at a remote station could select literally thousands of frequencies, all produced with a relatively small number of crystals. While the VHF radios of the day could tune 10 to 12 frequencies, the new UHF radios provided 1,750 channels. The ARC-27, as it was designated by the military, was a transceiver, which meant that it both transmitted and received on many of the same circuits.

The ARC-27 was developed by a group which included J. P. Giacoletto, M. R. Hubbard, and Horst Schweighofer. Most of the detailed mechanical and electrical designs were done by E. K. Vick, Fred Holm, John Goetz, Emil Martin, H. Lehman, and Gordon Nicholson.

The Collins engineers originally planned a production rate for the Navy of 500 radios per month. However, with the Air Force contract award also going to Collins Radio, the quota was set at 1,000 sets per month.

AN/ARC-27

At the end of the production line for the ARC-27.

Production began in late 1950, with the first 15 radios delivered to the military in January, 1951. By June, 1951, production reached 1,000 per month and continued at that level through September, 1952.

The success of the radio led to another military contract award to Collins — for UHF ground station radios to link with the airborne units. The Department of Defense had originally contracted a fourth manufacturer to build the ground station sets, but because of complications, Collins was asked to supply a complete redesign. Approximately 15,000 of the ground station UHF radios, called the GRC-27, were produced using the same design concepts as in the highly successful airborne units.

During the same period, the Korean conflict escalated, United States military support was sent to aid the South Korean government, and pressure was increased to build more ARC-27 radios. To meet the increased quotas, Western Electric was subcontracted to produce 10,000 radios under the Collins design. Another radio manufacturer, Admiral, also joined in the huge production effort and produced 25,000 Collins-designed UHF radios. In Cedar Rapids, Collins Radio assembly lines turned out a total of 40,000 ARC-27s. The radio was installed aboard almost every U.S. military aircraft operating in the 1950s.

The demands of rapid production made the ARC-27 a pressure program for Collins. Full production was at times delayed by parts shortages, caused by the nationwide industrial scramble for defense materials, by problems of personnel procurement and training, and by production and testing difficulties involved in building a new and highly complicated product.

"From a production standpoint, the difficulties which limited the accelerated production quotas boil down to two major ones," said John Dayhoff, production superintendent in a 1951 *Collins Column* article. "These were the training of inexperienced personnel and the shortage of parts."

By June, 1951, the problems were overcome and the increased production quotas were being met. In recognition of the achievement, a celebration was held with speeches by Arthur Collins and Commander R. J. Wayland, Naval inspection service, and the coronation of an ARC-27 assembly queen, Kathleen Newkirk. Glenn Johnson, director of industrial relations, served as master of ceremonies.

In his speech, Arthur Collins praised his employees for meeting the quotas, and took the opportunity to answer some of his critics in the industry.

"Going back to 1945, I might remind you that our company at that time redoubled its efforts in the development of special military equipment, including work which led to the ARC-27. We stressed special equipment development throughout the years when other companies in the industry were busy with conversion to civilian production and were happily building television sets and other home gadgets. Many people thought we were crazy to continue our old line of work. As a matter of fact, we did have several unprofitable years of operation, but we were successful in developing several very important equipments, probably more than any other electronics company."

The impact of the UHF radio contracts on the company was tremendous. In 1948, total sales were less than $8 million. In 1951, ARC-27 production totaled approximately $12 million, and in 1952 the figure increased to $24 million.

Installation of a Collins ARC-27 radio in an F-86 fighter jet.

Aviation Electronics

The second major post-war growth market for Collins Radio Company was in the field of civil aviation.

Before the war, a few airlines flourished with the widespread use of reliable and relatively comfortable airplanes such as the Douglas DC-2. Armed forces air shuttling during the war gave hundreds of thousands of persons their first taste of air travel, and there was no going back.

Another area of civil aviation development was business flying. American business sprouted wings at the close of World War II. Several reasons have been advanced for the post-war business flying boom. Air-mindedness was a primary cause, but it took a couple of catalysts to put companies in the flying business. One was the large number of surplus government planes — Lodestars, C47s (the military version of the DC-3), B-17s, B-25s, and others offered for sale at cut rates at the end of the war. The excess profits tax and favorable tax provisions for amortization made the heavy outlay for aircraft and air facilities less painful.

In the late 1940s and early 1950s, aircraft began operating in the improved communications and navigation environment brought on by advances in electronics technology. Air traffic control radar, instrument landing systems, and VHF communications aided in control and separation of aircraft operating in poor weather conditions. A new system of navigation called VOR (VHF omnidirectional range) was installed in ground stations across the country to replace the limited coverage, low frequency "beam" navigation system. The world's skies became more crowded with aircraft flying in worse weather conditions than ever before, causing a great increase in pilot workload, nearly approaching human limits.

Simple, easy to operate, reliable radio aids held a large part of the answer to the increased safety of air travel. Such electronics aids had to provide good position, steering, and weather information, with a minimum of attention and operating skill on the part of the pilot.

Recognizing the needs and the potential of the growing markets of business and commercial aviation, Collins moved to expand its aviation research and development. The Collins philosophy at the start of the effort was based on two key points: 1. Make it easy for the pilot. 2. Make the equipment so reliable that the chances of failure are extremely small. Collins engineers knew that only with this approach could the impulse to distrust "gadgets," mechanical or electronic, be overcome in the pilot's mind,

The Collins hangar at the Cedar Rapids Airport, May 1945.

In 1945, a company hangar was built at the Cedar Rapids Municipal Airport, south of the city, to house two new company airplanes. The facility was also built for flight testing and proving advanced designs in radio equipment by actual installation and use in aircraft, and for service to customers. *(Note: A staff of about 40 Research Division scientists, engineers, and laboratory assistants were moved to the facility in late 1945 to work in the laboratories adjacent to the hangar. Their work dealt primarily with new radio propagation techniques. (See Chapter 5.)*

Arthur Collins, Vernon Rittger and Clark Chandler picked up the company's second Beech Model 18 in Wichita, Kansas.

Excerpted from the August 14, 1977 *Cedar Rapids Gazette*

By Art Hough

About two years after he was graduated from Iowa State in 1932, Walt Wirkler went to work for Collins Radio.

"At that time there were 22 people, including me and the scrubwoman and Arthur Collins' father," Wirkler said.

Asked to tell a yarn or two about his flights with Arthur Collins, whom he characterized as "an excellent pilot," Wirkler came up with this one:

"The company had bought a Beechcraft in Wichita, Kan., and we were going down to get it, meeting a Braniff pilot who was to fly it up for us.

"We got Jim Wathan to fly us down in a Fairchild. We started out from Cedar Rapids in a helluva head wind. So we hugged the ground. It got so rough that Jim said:

" 'To hell with it. Let's take it up to 7,000 feet and buck the head wind. We'll have smooth air anyway.'

"He told me to take it up while he was looking up stuff on his maps. We'd just leveled off at 7,000 feet when the darned thing swallowed a valve.

"It was almost dark on the ground then, near Excelsior Springs, but at 7,000 feet we had time to look around. I finally figured we could land on a razorback ridge which was headed into the wind. But when I started heading it that way, Jim took another look.

" 'Supposing we got hurt and they couldn't get in there to get us out?' he said.

"So he took over and plopped us down in a little pasture with white-face cattle. They never even looked up, because we weren't making any noise. We had to get a farmer and his pickup truck and some rope and pull this thing into the corner and build a little fence around it.

"He took us to a road and Arthur and I hitchhiked to Excelsior Springs, got a bus to Kansas City, and an airline from there to Wichita. Jim got a ride with a hearse. He hitchhiked all the way home."

"You had to have a little sense of humor if you wanted to fly in those days. If you wanted to fly, you'd better not figure on getting to a certain place at a certain time. You might not get there at all."

Editor's note: Wirkler was prolific as an engineer and scientist for Collins between 1938 and the mid 1950s. He researched direction finder navigation, participated in early high-speed radio telegraphy studies, helped develop navigation computers, autopilots, instrument landing systems, and collaborated with Arthur Collins to develop the first horizontal situation indicator. He now lives in Garnavillo, Iowa.

One of the first developments from Collins for the new thrust into civilian aviation was a 100-watt, 20-channel, high frequency communications radio called the 18S. More than 500 were delivered in 1947, making Collins Radio the leading supplier of airborne radio equipment to the airlines. Important early customers for the 18S included American, Pan American, Northwest Orient, Braniff, Colonial, and Peruvian Airlines.

Also significant in the emergence of Collins as the leading supplier of airborne radio gear for the airlines was a new navigation receiver called the 51R. In 1946, Aeronautical Radio, Inc., a non-profit, research and communications company jointly owned by the major airlines, asked the radio industry for proposals on airborne receivers designed to meet the difficult specifications demanded by the new VOR system of navigation. Collins was one of six companies to comply and one of two whose designs were approved. The receiver equipped commercial transport planes for the new VOR navigation system being installed around the nation. In addition to the navigation function, the 51R was used to receive the localizer signal of an all-weather landing system. The localizer transmission defined the centerline of runways equipped with the new Instrument Landing System (ILS).

At this time, the company purchased from war surplus a Douglas C-47. The airplane was reconditioned and fitted with a model transport radio and pilot instrumentation setup. By using the C-47 in flight tests with its equipment, Collins acquired knowledge of flight problems and used that experience to design effective airborne equipment, including the 51R.

Above
The Collins 18S high frequency radio.

Lower Left
To flight test omnidirectional range equipment, Collins purchased a large Douglas C-47 from war surplus. 1947 photo.

Opposite Page

Upper Right
The Collins integrated flight system consisted of the radio box, the course indicator and the approach horizon.

Lower Right
The approach horizon instrument and a smaller version of the course indicator as they appeared in a cockpit. The integrated flight system instruments are second from the left.

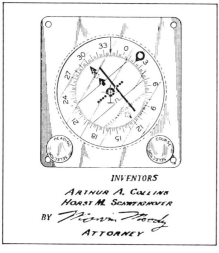

INVENTORS

ARTHUR A. COLLINS
HORST M. SCHWEIGHOFER

BY *Marvin Moody*

ATTORNEY

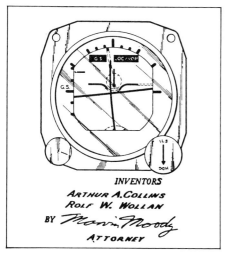

INVENTORS

ARTHUR A. COLLINS
ROLF W. WOLLAN

BY *Marvin Moody*

ATTORNEY

One of the key Collins engineers who developed new aviation equipment was Francis L. Moseley. As a U.S. Army colonel during the war, Moseley developed the instrument approach system used by the military for blind landings, and was the principle designer of the Collins 51R.

To help the pilot cope with the increasingly complex problems of flying, Arthur Collins and his associates worked to develop a new flight director system, which was introduced in 1950. The Collins Integrated Flight System had several unique features provided by the instruments and a steering computer.

Radio navigation information was displayed on a course deviation bar, but unlike previous systems, this bar was superimposed on a compass card enabling the pilot to visualize directly his angular relationship to a selected course. This marked the birth of the horizontal situation indicator (HSI), which has been applied over the years in nearly every aircraft application, from private airplanes to jumbo jets to the Space Shuttle. The first HSI was patented by Arthur Collins and Horst Schweighofer, based on an idea by consultant Siegfried Knemeyer.

The HSI was paired with an attitude direction indicator which provided an artificial horizon with steering information superimposed. The new system replaced five cockpit instruments with two, and gave the pilot a clear pictorial presentation of the information he needed for enroute navigation and precise instrument landings. The Collins flight director system freed the pilot from several mental computations, allowing him to do his essential job of flying more effectively. For example, the steering computer automatically corrected for crosswinds encountered during a landing approach.

Collins engineers and salesmen toured the country in the company's Twin Beech D-18 equipped with the new system and were met with enthusiastic receptions. The August, 1952, edition of *Flight* magazine quoted a chief pilot as calling it "a pilot's dream . . . the most complete and simplest instrumentation yet perfected to assist pilots in overcoming the problems of low approaches."

The first sale of the system was for a converted B-25 owned by Albert Trostel and Sons of Milwaukee, Wis., and it was installed by Associated Radio Co., Collins Radio's distributor in Dallas, Texas. By 1952, Collins had received orders for 50 of the systems, which sold for about $4,000 each, and 1953 production was set at 1,000 systems.

The business aviation market was the first to embrace the new system, largely because owners of business aircraft were not encumbered by requirements to standardize equipment, and therefore could adopt new products more easily than could the commercial airlines.

By 1955, the airlines were also using the Collins flight director system. The first major airline application was aboard the Vickers Viscount airliner, chosen by Trans-Canada, Trans-Australian, Air France, Capital, and several others.

Using bearing information from two VOR stations, a navigation computer developed by Collins was a predecessor to today's area navigation systems.

In 1954, Collins introduced its first autopilot for automatic control in cross-country flight and during ILS approaches to airports. The AP-101 was designed to work with the flight director system so the pilot could continuously monitor the approach. The combination was an entirely new method of automatic flying which gave the pilot a continuous and easily understood picture during automatic control, yet allowed him to take over at any time and manually fly with the same flight director instruments.

Collins built several types of aircraft antennas to accommodate all of its airborne equipment. The most widely known antenna of the period was the "deerhorn" navigation antenna, so named because of its distinctive shape. Used with the 51R VOR receiver, more than 10,000 deerhorns were installed atop the cockpits of most non-jet commercial

An early commercial airliner to have the Collins integrated flight system was the Vickers Viscount.

"It was a dandy shot, Swedley! I got him just as he lifted his wheels at La Guardia."

This cartoon in the December, 1951 Collins Column found humor in the shape of the "deerhorn" airborne antenna. It was drawn by Richard Pinney, now an artist in the Cedar Rapids area.

CNI units were developed for new generation military jet aircraft.

airliners, business, and military planes in the United States. The deerhorn was developed in 1948 by Collins engineer John Shanklin.

Collins introduced its first weather radar system in 1955. Delta Air Lines was first to install Collins WP-101 weather radar. Delta also chose two other new systems: automatic direction finding equipment, and Selcal, which permitted ground stations to call specific airplanes. The $1.5 million order from Delta came shortly after the airline was awarded new routes from Atlanta to New York, and from New Orleans to Houston.

Collins weather radar systems were designed to be installed in large airplanes, but a Dallas television station, WFAA-TV, installed a system at its studio in 1958, and became the first to present local weather by radar to a television audience.

The transponder was another avionics unit introduced to aviation in the mid-1950s. As an aid for air traffic control, the Collins transponder provided a signal which reinforced ground radar to permit positive identification by the air traffic controller.

In the late 1950s, the new F-4 Phantom generation of military jets presented new problems for electronics manufacturers. High-speed aircraft requiring electronic equipment capable of operating under severe environmental conditions led to the development of a new concept known as CNI (communication, navigation and identification) systems engineering.

Before the CNI systems approach, electronic equipment specifications did not keep pace with new aircraft designs. Consequently, outmoded equipment was often delivered for newly-designed planes. The Collins CNI system was a tailor-made group of standardized electronic modules which provided communication, navigation, and identification functions for a particular type of aircraft. The modules had standarized electrical, mechanical and thermal connections which permitted the same modules to be assembled into different units, as required for each particular aircraft.

By 1966, Collins had installed more than $110 million worth of CNI equipment on more than 4,600 aircraft, including the Republic F-105 and the North American A3J.

Other post-war markets

While military UHF radios and aviation equipment were the primary growth products for Collins Radio in the eight years immediately following the war, other products were also developed.

An early contract for Collins CNI equipment was for installation aboard the U.S. Navy's A3J Vigilante, built by North American Aviation.

71

Sales resumed in amateur radio gear, the original product line of the company. The first Collins post-war amateur radio unit went to its new owner Jan. 8, 1947, during a formal ceremony held in the lobby of the Collins Main Plant. Clyde Hendrix, division president of Pillsbury Mills, Inc., purchased the new 30K transmitter and 75A receiver. The Clinton, Iowa, ham had been one of Arthur Collins' first customers in the 1930s, and placed his order for the new equipment sight unseen.

Lab assistant Kenneth Everhart stands beside a 30K-1 amateur transmitter. Seated is Nobel Hale, advertising editorial assistant, with a 310Z amateur band exciter. A color version of this photograph was featured on the cover of the November 1946 issue of Radio News.

The 30K transmitter, designed by engineer Warren Bruene, was of entirely new design and incorporated many new features for the ham community. Its companion receiver, the 75A, was one of several units at Collins which resulted from ideas which were being shaped for military applications just before the war ended. The basic idea was to achieve stability and accuracy in the reception of radio signals. The receiver employed an invention called the permeability-tuned oscillator (PTO), which improved frequency control to such close limits that the older method was no longer necessary.

During a demonstration of the new PTO at a ham radio

convention in 1947, Ted Hunter, who designed it, was showing the oscillator to a group of engineers. The presentation consisted of independently setting two pieces of equipment to the same dial frequency and then demonstrating frequency separation by means of the resulting beat note. Hunter liked to make the adjustments with the audio output cut off, then turned up the output so the beat note was clearly audible, "sort of a blindfold test."

One incredulous individual wanted to try it for himself. He set the independent oscillators, turned on the equipment, heard the beat note and walked away with a vague, puzzled look on his face. Twice more he returned to repeat the test while Hunter stood by trying to hold back a grin. As the puzzled individual walked away from the demonstration for the third time, he was heard to mutter, "By gosh, I guess that ad was right!" Such was the quality of Collins amateur equipment: nonbelievers became believers.

Broadcast equipment

Commercial radio stations enjoyed their golden age during the 1930s, and just prior to the war, development work in television was under way. After World War II, some companies which had previously specialized in radio transmitters turned their attention to television equipment, assuming the pictures and sound would replace the "sound-only" form of communication. Television did enjoy phenomenal growth after the war, but broadcast radio equipment continued to account for a large volume of business for Collins Radio.

Nearly 350 new radio stations went on the air between 1951 and 1955. One of the most numerous types was in the medium power category, with towns as small as 4,000 population getting their first radio stations. The Collins 20V was one of the best sellers in that category, with sales near 300 by 1955. Lauren Findley was the original project engineer for the 20V. Collins furnished complete AM and FM radio stations, including everything from the announcer's microphone to the station antenna.

Collins Radio designed and built a line of FM transmitters, offering the choice of a 250-watt, one-kilowatt, three-kilowatt, or ten-kilowatt transmitter as standard equipment. At the 1949 National Association of Broadcasters conference, John Green, head of broadcast sales for Collins, presented a paper describing how the Autopositioner could be used for remote control of broadcast transmitters. One year later Collins Radio introduced a one-kilowatt AM transmitter featuring a new circuit design which improved reliability and operation.

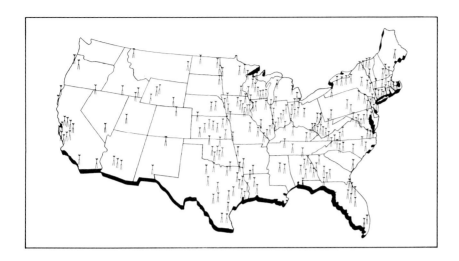

By 1948, Collins broadcast transmitters were being used at many radio stations across the country, as depicted by the symbols. Hundreds of others employed speech, studio or other equipment manufactured by the company.

Although the company never entered the consumer radio receiver market on any large scale, an effort was made to market a less expensive version of the famous Autotune for home radio receivers. The 496E Autotune was less precise and therefore less expensive than the military and commercial versions, but its price tag proved too much for even the top-of-the-line home radios.

However, another type of broadcast radio receiver manufactured by Collins was successful: a receiver engineered expressly for railroads. The problems peculiar to railroad installations, such as fading signals and interference, were worked out in cooperation with the Rock Island Railroad and the American Phenolic Corporation. The project, which was started in 1945, produced a broadcast receiver and distribution system for clear reception in railroad cars. The system provided reception of any one of ten predetermined broadcast stations, and tape or wire recorders could be used in conjunction with the receiver to furnish a pleasing variety of programs for passengers.

The control room of radio station WMT in Cedar Rapids contained Collins broadcast equipment.

Another area of broadcast radio equipment for Collins Radio Company in the post-war years was equipment for the State Department's Voice of America network.

In the conflict of ideologies with the Communist block countries, later coined the "Cold War," the weapon was radio. In 1950, the VOA began an expansion program to lengthen its radio time, add 19 languages to its former 26,

Test technicians C. F. Hardenbrook, left, and Hank Rathje consult schematics while "troubleshooting" one of the large 207B-1 transmitters used by the Voice of America. 1951 photo.

and increase the effectiveness of its signal. Collins Radio had a big part in equipping the radio ship *Courier* for its debut in the propaganda war. The project, called "Operation Vagabond," was a facet of the "ring plan" designed to ring all of the world's critical areas with extremely high-power communication facilities. The biggest obstacle faced by the VOA was the electrical field created by an estimated 1,250 Soviet jamming transmitters.

Aboard the *Courier,* Collins field engineers installed two 35-kilowatt shortwave transmitters and a 3-kilowatt transmitter for ship-to-shore communications. An RCA 150-kilowatt transmitter was used for medium wave. Banks of Collins receivers were also used at relay stations to pick up the stateside broadcasts for relay across eastern Europe.

Despite the Kremlin's best efforts, in 1952 the VOA signals could be heard 25 percent of the time inside Moscow, where

75

the jamming was concentrated, and 60 to 80 percent of the time outside the Soviet capital.

Post-war impact

Even though much of the company's employment growth had occurred earlier, Collins Radio had the greatest impact on its host community beginning in approximately 1948.

During the war most of the plant workers either commuted to Cedar Rapids, or were local residents who had previously worked at companies which were not war plants, or were entering the work force for the first time. Because of wartime restrictions, housing construction was at a virtual standstill.

Following the adjustment period at the close of the war, a pent-up housing industry exploded in Cedar Rapids, especially on the north side near the Collins Main Plant. Many commuters moved to town and many new employees moved to Cedar Rapids, presenting a tremendous challenge for home builders, utilities, the school system, and the city.

"There was tremendous expansion in northeast Cedar Rapids and Collins was single-handedly responsible for that growth," said Harold Ewoldt, long-time Chamber of Commerce manager and local historian. "Collins had 'used up' the available work force, then came the boom in housing as workers came in from outside the area. The whole northeast part of Cedar Rapids in the triangle from First Avenue to Collins, plus growth in Marion, is due to Collins Radio."

In 1947, construction began on an 80,000-square-foot building south of the Main Plant to house the finishing department. The paints and solvents used by the finishing department had been causing problems with the air-conditioning system in the Main Plant; the addition also was undertaken to consolidate several scattered departments.

Construction of Building 139 behind the Main Plant as it appeared on October 27, 1947, looking southwest.

The Collins Main Plant area as it appeared from the north in 1950. The tent at the rear of the site was erected to cover the assembly area for a large dish antenna (see Chapter 5). The area at the top of the photograph was used as a trailer park during World War II, but by 1950, most of the trailers had been removed.

5
New ideas

While much of the post-war research effort at Collins Radio Company was applied to specific products such as UHF military radios and aviation electronics, a separate division was formed to undertake research in general fields of study, without the pressures of contract deadlines and restrictions. Significant scientific developments in electronic communication, atomic research, and flight control came out of this research work at Collins.

Starting in 1946, Collins had under study, both independently and in conjunction with government agencies and labs, new methods of reliable, long distance communication. Out of this investigation emerged what was known as Transhorizon communication techniques: methods by which VHF and UHF signals were transmitted beyond the line of sight. Many of the achievements in Transhorizon techniques were outgrowths of advanced work with a high-power transmitting tube known as the Resnatron.

The Resnatron principle was originally developed in 1938 by Winfield Salisbury (Cedar Rapids native and friend of Arthur Collins) and two associates at the University of California. The scientists were attempting to find a solution to the problem of obtaining high power outputs at extremely high frequencies. Like so many other scientific projects, the Resnatron was pressed into military service during World War II. An urgent need arose, in connection with the radar countermeasures program at Harvard's radio research laboratory, for vacuum tubes capable of generating high power levels at frequencies in the range from 350 to 650 megacycles. This program culminated in the development of the Resnatron, which was used to jam airborne interceptor radar equipment carried by German night fighters over the English Channel.

When it became evident in 1947 that it would be necessary to assign UHF channels for television broadcasting due to a shortage of VHF channels, the government considered the possibility of adapting the Resnatron for television transmitter purposes. In view of these circumstances, Salisbury was hired as director of research at Collins to continue his

Collins engineer Irv H. Gerks tests a milling machine by shaping a small parabolic ''dish'' antenna. The machine was later used to shape a 50-foot-diameter dish antenna.

Resnatron studies. Much of the initial experimentation was performed by S. G. McNees, W. J. Armstrong, and Roger Borne of the research division staff.

To demonstrate the potential of the Resnatron for a variety of uses, Salisbury had the equipment rigged to produce microwaves of such intensity that they could cook a hamburger in 30 seconds or pop a sack of popcorn almost instantly. He demonstrated his "electronic oven" at the 1949 Iowa State Fair as one of the centennial exhibits in the Des Moines Register and Tribune building, and the device received much attention. Collins Radio, however, never developed a production model. Other companies, notably Raytheon, developed microwave ovens of their own design.

Upper
Dr. Walter Kohl (right), head of the vacuum tube laboratory at Collins Radio, and Dr. John Clark, senior engineer, discuss the new Resnatron tube which the company constructed.

Lower
The vacuum tube laboratory, part of the Collins research division, worked with new designs for high-power transmitting tubes. The man at the glass lathe is John Barton.

For Collins Radio, the more serious applications of Resnatron research dealt with electronic communications.

Faced with the difficult problem of deciding how far apart to place UHF stations on the same wavelength, the Federal Communications Commission selected Collins Radio to make the measurements because of the availability of its Resnatron equipment at its laboratory at the Cedar Rapids airport. DuMont Laboratories, CBS and RCA also investigated other aspects of UHF broadcasting.

At Collins, Irvin H. Gerks, nationally-known radio propagation expert, headed field studies at a number of remote locations approximately 100 miles from the Resnatron transmitter at the airport. Something unanticipated, and "rather startling," according to Gerks, was the discovery that on some summer mornings the signal received from Cedar Rapids seemed to be well within line-of-sight range, even though the portable receiving station was positioned well beyond the curvature of the earth.

But as the day wore on, the signal arrived weaker, presumably from scattering in the lower portion of the atmosphere, called the troposphere. The discovery led to development of a new form of radio communication known as scatter propagation.

Another area of radio research dealt with cosmic rays, which were microwaves emanating from the sun and other celestrial objects. In 1949 Collins researchers built a heavy power field station at a site called the Feather Ridge Observatory, situated along the Palo road near the Crawford stone quarry northwest of Cedar Rapids. One of the first experiments conducted at Feather Ridge was observation of a total eclipse of the moon through radio telescopes — the first time this had ever been done. From this experiment, Collins engineers observed that the lunar microwave temperature did not differ greatly from periods of direct sunlight on the moon's surface. This led to the conclusion that lunar radiation came not only from the surfaces, but also from layers of materials beneath the surface — far enough below the surface that the temperature remained constant.

The Feather Ridge studies, by Dr. Dale McCoy and C. M. Hepperle, led to construction by Collins of a giant aluminum dish antenna for the Naval Laboratory at Anacostia, D.C., in 1950. The 50-foot parabolic receiver, which was then the largest ever built, was used by the laboratory in its investigation of radio waves originating from celestial bodies.

"It has long been known that there is a connection between the activity of the sun and long-distance radio communication between any two points on the earth. To further

Dr. Gene Marner with a radio telescope at the Feather Ridge facility.

One distinguished scientist to come to Collins Radio Company in the post-war period was Dr. Alexander Lippisch.

His Delta I glider, built in 1930, was converted into a powered plane and shown in flight to the public in 1931. Lippisch further developed his idea and designed the first high-speed rocket-powered aircraft, the ME 163 Komet, which flew 625 miles per hour for the German Luftwaffe in 1941.

A model of his swept-back Delta glider, together with results of his research, showed the superiority of this type of high-speed aircraft, used today in many jet fighter designs.

As Nazi Germany collapsed in the spring of 1945, the United States raced in to grab as many of the highly skilled German scientists as possible. Under code name "Operation Paperclip," Dr. Lippisch was one of 50 German scientists brought to the United States.

Dr. Lippisch joined Collins Radio in February, 1950, as head of aerodynamical research. It was here that he developed the Aerodyne, an unusual wingless aircraft. The Aerodyne project, funded by the Office of Naval Research, took place in the Collins Aeronautical Research Laboratory at the Cedar Rapids airport, and ultimately a full size non-flying "test bed" was constructed. The test model wasn't intended to fly, but the Navy insisted for continued funding that it must fly, so an engine and propeller were added. The craft was shipped to Moffet Field near Sunnyvale, California, for wind tunnel testing, and there the project was scuttled in 1962.

At the Collins Aeronautical Research Lab, Dr. Lippisch also developed an advanced smoke tunnel to study the flow of air over airfoils.

At the conclusion of the aerodynamic studies at Collins, Dr. Lippisch's efforts switched to another project initiated by Arthur Collins — boat hull research.

Collins was looking for ways to improve efficiency in planing hulls.

In 1959, aerodynamics lab personnel were moved to a new laboratory in the Butler Buildings near the Main Plant. The test area was equipped with a 90-foot-long, 12,000 gallon tow tank for testing scale models of new hull designs. A glass window in the bottom of the tank permitted

Upper Right
Dr. Lippisch, seated at control console, demonstrates a flying model of the Aerodyne to a tour group at the Collins hangar. The model used electric motors to force air downward to create lift.

Middle Right
The two-dimensional smoke tunnel designed by Dr. Lippisch was acclaimed as one of the finest available for studying airflow over airfoils.

Lower Right
The Aeroboat was flown successfully several times at the Coralville Reservoir by pilot Clayton Lander.

Lower
This full-scale "test bed" of the Aerodyne never flew, but was built to test the design principles of Dr. Lippisch's unique flying machine.

photographs to be made of the flow pattern which resulted from movement of the model through the water. A two dimensional flow tunnel — one of the first of its kind — was constructed to investigate flow without the complications of side or end effects.

Five to six persons performed research at the marine lab, while a group of 15 persons constructed models and full-scale boats.

From 1960 to 1962, several boats were built at the lab, and operational tests were performed on Cedar Lake and the Cedar River. The design efforts in Cedar Rapids culminated in 1962 with construction in Newport Beach, California, of a 72-foot fiberglass boat, now owned by Arthur Collins.

The advanced designs produced at the marine lab were never adopted by the boat manufacturing industry, largely because the deep "V" hull was designed at about the same time, and provided good turning and handling characteristics along with good performance at high speeds.

In 1963, the Collins marine lab, under the supervision of Dr. Lippisch, designed and built the Aeroboat. The craft was the first ever designed to use the ground effect principle over a body of water. The wooden experimental craft was originally licensed as a boat, but after a few tests, it became apparent that it would fly as an airplane. Test pilot Clayton Lander called the FAA and told them the Collins Aeroboat might need to be reclassified as an airplane.

"When do we become an airplane?" Lander asked the FAA officials. They studied the question for several days and reported back to the Collins group that if it flew more than 28 inches off the surface of the water, it should be reclassified as an airplane. Since the Aeroboat had flown more than 100 feet high, it became an airplane.

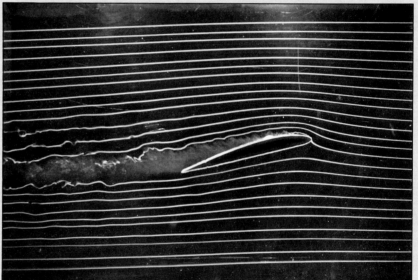

The original wooden craft is now on display at the Experimental Aircraft Association museum in Milwaukee. After Dr. Lippisch's retirement from Collins in 1964, he worked with other firms to refine Aeroboat principles. Dr. Lippisch died in 1976 at age 81.

National attention was drawn to another research project in November, 1951. Scientists from Collins and the National Bureau of Standards used the moon as a giant reflector to bounce UHF signals from Cedar Rapids, Iowa, to Sterling, Virginia.

"The experiments indicate the feasibility of using the moon as a natural relay station for radio communications between two points on the earth's surface," explained Arthur Collins. Specially constructed for the experiment was a 75-foot "tapered wave guide horn" antenna, installed at the Collins hangar at the Cedar Rapids Airport. Shaped like a huge funnel, the antenna directed the radio signals to the moon. On the trip back to earth the signals were received by a 30-foot dish reflector installed at Sterling by the National Bureau of Standards. Using a 20-kilowatt transmitter with power generated by the Resnatron tube, the coded signal was sent the one-half million miles from earth to moon to earth. When the signal was decoded in Sterling it revealed a message that had been heard in the vicinity before. It was the historic message, "What hath God wrought!", used by Samuel Morse in 1844 over his new telegraph line from Washington to Baltimore.

The Collins-NBS experiment was the first time a long distance message had been sent via the moon, and was the first use of UHF frequencies for this purpose. (Six years earlier the Army Signal Corps successfully bounced an unintelligible radio signal off the moon.)

In 1952, Collins installed an experimental communication link between its Cedar Rapids Airport laboratory and its new Dallas laboratory. *(See Chapter 6)* The link served as a field test facility for the Collins Predicted Wave Teletype system in long-range point-to-point service. In addition, the Cedar Rapids-Dallas link was used for research and investigation of various modulation techniques including the comparison of voice transmission by narrowband FM and a system called single sideband.

Two years later, Collins established a tropospheric scatter circuit between the engineering building in Cedar Rapids and a terminal near Lamar, Missouri. The Lamar terminal was located on a direct line halfway between the Cedar Rapids terminal and the Dallas facility.

Collins Radio gained the attention of the news media in April, 1950, when the *New York Times* reported on the Transhorizon experiments being conducted by Collins. The feature-length article described the discovery of "a new way of sending radio signals through the air that holds the promise of revolutionizing long-distance communication, and

In 1947, under a contract with the Atomic Energy Commission, the first commercially-built cyclotron began as a project of Collins Radio Company. For the first time, construction of an "atom smasher" was put on a production budget and certain standards of performance were guaranteed. The accelerator was delivered to the AEC's Brookhaven National Laboratory on Long Island.

When it received the $750,000 cyclotron contract from the AEC, Collins Radio was the first firm to enter the field. General Electric was the only competitor. There were many such devices in use in the United States and other countries, but all were hand-made and no standards of performance had to be guaranteed. Manufacturing a cyclotron on a production schedule was something new. The job had to be done with the skills and tools of a private concern rather than the manpower and facilities of the large universities.

The high energy machines were regarded as holding great prospects in the field of medicine for cancer therapy and in the field of energy for development of atomic power sources.

The most bulky item in the Collins cyclotron was the 250-ton magnet, cast by the Carnegie-Illinois Steel Company. The coils were wound by Collins workers at the main plant. Aluminum stripping as wide as a man's palm was used. Problems arose in assembling the "dees," the copper vacuum chambers in which the atomic fragments spin. When the massive tubes were placed in the Collins 250-ton hydraulic press to flatten out the ends to form the vacuum chamber, the jaws of the giant press just bounced. Collins technicians finally rigged up an arrangement of ganged levers, powered by a hydraulic jack, which squeezed the ends to the desired shape. Welding copper also proved to be a difficult chore. Collins developed a technique using helium and a tungsten arc which did the job.

Atomic particles injected into the machine's center were accelerated by electric forces and steered by the magnet into a spiral path which brought them to the target area. The specimen target, being bombarded by

Winfield Salisbury displays a model of the atom-smasher built for the Atomic Energy Commission at Brookhaven National Laboratory on Long Island.

particles, was made radioactive. In other words, the cyclotron gave high speed to particles and used them as projectiles for nuclear disintegration.

One of the outstanding features of the Collins cyclotrons was the large number of high-speed particles they produced — about a million billion per second. Expressed in terms of conventional current units (for each particle carried a charge of electricity) the output was 200 millionths of an ampere.

A second cyclotron, very similar to the one made for Brookhaven, was completed in 1952 by Collins for the Argonne National Laboratory at Lemont, Illinois near Chicago. The facility was designed, constructed, installed and adjusted to full performance by Collins Radio at a cost to the lab of $966,000. More than a dozen scientists and technicians, under the direction of Dr. J. J. Livengood, accomplished the second and final installation of a Collins cyclotron.

In October, 1951, Dr. Livengood announced his resignation from Collins to accept a position at the Argonne Laboratories, to direct use of the cyclotron.

Upper
Two exciter coils near completion for the 250-ton magnet of the Brookhaven cyclotron. Each coil contained nearly three miles of hollow, water-cooled aluminum strap.

Middle
The control room of the Collins cyclotron at Brookhaven.

Lower
The completed cyclotron at the Brookhaven National Laboratory.

conceivably might open the door to international televison. The new method appears to make obsolete the generally accepted theory that signals transmitted on very high frequencies, such as those used by video, are limited to line of sight.''

The Collins researchers discounted the possibility of using their techniques for international television because of signal quality problems. But they agreed that Transhorizon techniques could revolutionize long-distance communication.

More experiments and achievements followed. In 1953 Collins designed and constructed a 50-kilowatt biconical and pyramidal antenna for the Air Research and Development Command at Prospect Hill, New Jersey. The 8,000-pound aluminum antenna was used in research work of the Air Force's Cambridge Research Center.

This pioneering work enabled Collins to have a complete line of Transhorizon equipment ready in the mid-1950s when the Distant Early Warning (DEW) Line was established.

With Russia's first explosion of an atomic bomb in 1949 and the invasion of South Korea in 1950, American leaders realized the need for an electronic early warning system to detect intruding aircraft approaching through the Arctic. To be effective, the DEW Line had to coordinate its many parts. Conventional high frequency communication equipment dependent upon ionospheric refraction could not be relied upon because of the frequent blackouts and disturbances in the Arctic caused by magnetic storms, aurora borealis, sun spots and other phenomena. Land lines or microwave relays were out of the question in this Arctic desert because of the cost.

The answer came with the development of Collins Transhorizon, or scatter, communications. By means of high-powered transmitters, high-gain antennas and sensitive receivers, Transhorizon systems were able to use the scatter effect in VHF and UHF radio wave propagation to achieve highly persistent communication beyond the horizon. The equipment was used to tie the DEW Line with the continental defense complex, and to connect the DEW Line stations with each other.

Behind the scenes of these publicized developments, a similar project was kept under security wraps. Dr. Dale McCoy, who was instrumental in much of the cosmic ray antenna research, designed a new navigation device based on those principles.

Within a year after publications appeared in 1944 and 1945 describing weak microwave radiation emitted by the sun, Collins began research into radio astronomy, and shortly

An early version of the Collins radio sextant, at the Feather Ridge Observatory.

afterward investigated the feasibility of an all-weather sextant, an electronic counterpart to the hand-held optical sextant which depended on a clear sky. Most of the research was conducted at the Feather Ridge facility. Dr. McCoy, R. M. Ringeon, and C. M. Hepperle were largely responsible for the development of the world's first radio sextant.

While the optical sextant used direct light waves from the sun to determine the ship's position, the Collins radio sextant used radio waves from the sun. The sun's radio waves easily penetrate the clouds, enabling all-weather operation of the radio sextant in the daytime.

Collins Radio project engineer Ted Willis discusses features of the radio sextant with Capt. John Brandt and Lt. John Kuncas of the U.S. Navy. The instrument was installed aboard the USS Compass Island *in 1959. U.S. Navy photograph.*

Announcement of the radio sextant in the summer of 1954 again drew nationwide attention to Collins Radio. Captain P. V. H. Weems, chairman of the board, Aeronautical Services, Inc., visited Cedar Rapids shortly after the announcement. He commented, "The opportunity to inspect and test the original Collins automatic radio sextant has convinced me that we are entering a new and extended phase of practical celestial navigation."

Time magazine, in an interview with Fred Haddock, radio astronomer of the Naval Research Laboratory, reported: "The ship's navigator can find his position just as if he had an assistant watching the sun through an ordinary optical sextant. No cloudy weather gets in the way of the radio sextant, nor can an enemy jam the radio impulses (as is possible with other radio aids to navigation, such as Loran)."

The first radio sextant detected only energy from the sun, which restricted its effectiveness to daylight hours. However, as advances were made and a more sensitive antenna and receiver were developed, a sextant was built which could track both sun and moon.

6

Growth in the 1950s

The decade of the 1950s was a period of spectacular growth for Collins Radio Company, and the electronics industry in general. In 1950, total company employment was about 2,000. By 1959 that figure had reached nearly 11,000. Annual sales of less than $13 million in 1950 soared to $118 million by the end of the decade.

Collins received growing recognition in all its markets, especially in the burgeoning areas of microwave communications, single sideband, and aviation electronics.

Writing in the New York edition of *Commercial and Financial Chronicle,* Philip Carret, a New York Stock Exchange broker, assessed the condition of Collins Radio Company at the beginning of the 1950s:

"As a consequence of this high regard for the company's products, Collins' backlog, which has risen $100 million in the past year, continues to grow. It is currently reported to be in excess of $150 million. During World War II the rate of shipments was $5 million a month. At the presently increased level of prices and with greatly expanded factory facilities, a higher level of output can obviously be expected.

"The Collins management does not consider that this huge increase in business on the books is merely a reflection of the rearmament boom. A far-sighted policy of emphasizing research and development was adopted after V-J Day and a considerable part of the current backlog is attributable to demand for improved and wholly new products which would have been ordered even under normal conditions. The size of the present backlog is a tribute to Collins' engineering, research, and far-sighted management. However, there is no reason to believe that the backlog has by any means reached its peak. Air Force requirements are steadily being expanded and the trend in electronic equipment is toward more complex and expensive equipment."

Starting in 1950, Collins Radio Company undertook a five-year, $5 million program of fixed asset investment, which included new laboratory and manufacturing facilities. In the first two years of the program, the company doubled its floor space, and more expansion followed.

Much of the steel framework was in place by June 1953 for the new engineering building (Building 120) in Cedar Rapids. The unpaved road at the bottom of the photograph is C Avenue.

The Cherry Building was located at 317 10th Avenue SE in Cedar Rapids.

Part of Collins Radio's new research division was moved in the summer of 1950 to a leased three-story building, formerly the site of the Cherry-Burrell Corporation's factory in Cedar Rapids. The large structure was also used as a warehouse for overflow and obsolete stock.

In April, 1951, the purchasing department moved from the Main Plant to a building on Second Avenue near Fifth Street in Cedar Rapids. The purchasing department occupied the lower two floors, and the upper floor housed a training school for military radio men. The industrial engineering department took over the area at the Main Plant left by the purchasing department.

National business publications reported that the electronics industry was due for vast expansion. The military procurement logjam had broken wide open, and the govern-

For a time, women "white room" employees at the Main Plant wore head coverings called "snoods" to keep hairs out of delicate flight instruments. But some managers thought visitors got the erroneous impression that only nuns worked in the white room, so the snoods were replaced with caps. 1952 photo.

Doris Gilbert Werth (front) and Edith Atkinson set type on the Collins publications department's Justowriter machines. The department was located in the Third Street Building. 1957 photo.

ment agreed to bigger tax deductions for some manufacturers who were turning out products for the armed forces. Those firms included big names such as RCA, Westinghouse and General Electric, and specialty manufacturers such as Federal Telephone & Radio and Collins Radio Company. Uncle Sam began to string radar stations around the United States and Canadian coastlines, airfields were reactivated, and naval vessels were pulled out of "mothballs." Modernized tanks and other vehicles of modern warfare used radio and other electronic equipment. The Pentagon wanted the electronics industry able to multiply its output in case another big war started.

With increasing military orders, Collins was urged by the Defense Department to consider further decentralization of its facilities for security reasons. Management began studies of a number of communities. Collins Radio announced in May, 1951, an expansion program to build a $1 million plant near the Dallas, Texas, suburb of Richardson. Another Dallas building was leased to start mechanical assembly production while the new plant was under construction. Collins also announced plans to lease a hangar at nearby Redbird Airport to install and repair airborne equipment.

Most all employees for the plant came from the Dallas area. James Flynn, Jr., was named general manager. Flynn came from American Airlines where, as superintendent of communications, he ordered Collins Autotune equipment for the American Airlines fleet in 1937. By June, 1951, three other managers had been assigned to the Dallas facility. W. G. Pap-

Part of the Texas Division was located in this leased building on Hi Line Drive in Dallas.

penfus was named director of manufacturing, Harold Moss was made manager of test and inspection, and Arthur Luebs was named senior buyer for the Texas Division.

"Our decision to locate the new plant in Texas is in line with the current practice of separating production plants geographically for security reasons," Arthur Collins explained. "So long as we are locating another plant away from our main operation, we picked a place close to the heart of the aviation industry, and where the weather would give us more uniform test flight conditions. We found exactly the conditions we were looking for in Texas."

The new one-story, 50,000-square-foot plant was similar in design to the main plant in Cedar Rapids but was about half the size.

With the announcement of the Dallas facility, the company also made plans to expand operations at the regional sales office in Burbank with another 10,000-square-feet and additional employees, and to add new equipment at the Main Plant and Cherry-Burrell building in Cedar Rapids. The federal government granted Collins a five-year tax writeoff for about $800,000 of the projects.

Actually, the company at first did not intend to expand the Burbank plant. Collins had originally announced in December, 1950, plans to build a new $500,000 plant in Arcadia,

The first Western Division production facility was located in Burbank, California.

California for research and manufacturing. The Arcadia Chamber of Commerce and a local citizens' committee wanted the Collins plant in their town, but a vocal group of Arcadia residents opposed the new plant. They presented a petition which said a new Collins plant would set a precedent for more factories in the predominantly residential suburb of Los Angeles, would provide a strategic bombing site, and would increase traffic and smog. The Arcadia City Council voted three-to-two to turn down the Collins request for rezoning, so the plan was dropped in January, 1951. Instead, the Burbank facility was expanded and made headquarters of the new Western Division of Collins Radio Company.

The first contract for the Western Division, located at 2700 West Olive Avenue in Burbank, was a testing job for the Atomic Energy Commission. The first production job and the beginning of an assembly line was for the construction of servo amplifiers and drive units for Lockheed Aircraft Service. Later projects included guided missile receivers, a navigation trainer for the Navy, a voice/code reproducer for the Civil Aeronautics Administration, and general production overflow from the Main Plant in Cedar Rapids. A major function of the Western Division was to aid aircraft manufacturers in the California area in determining their radio and electronic needs, and to service Collins equipment in that area. Carl Service, who had previously been Collins Radio's service manager on the west coast, was made the first Western Division manager.

New engineering building

In May, 1952, the company submitted an application to the federal government for a certificate of necessity covering construction and amortization (for tax purposes) of a new engineering building in Cedar Rapids (now called Building 120). The certificate was approved that autumn, and Collins announced that a $1.8 million engineering laboratory was to be built to house approximately 600 employees in 12 labs and additional office space. Other space was to be provided for a lobby, technical library and a cafeteria-auditorium. The site was a 52-acre wooded tract at the intersection of Old Marion Road and C Avenue, just northeast of Cedar Rapids. At that time, engineering activities in Cedar Rapids were scattered at a number of locations. The new plant was designed to concentrate most engineering at a single site.

An existing mortgage-loan agreement was extended to finance construction. Under terms of the agreement, Collins Radio put up as collateral real estate and buildings owned by

the company in Cedar Rapids as well as machinery and equipment. The Linn County Board of Supervisors paved the way for construction in October, 1951, by approving a zoning change from residential to light industrial. With all formalities cleared, Collins exercised options it held on the land, and Marie Carver and her son, Weston, sold the tract to Collins.

The following March, the City of Cedar Rapids expanded by 52 acres when it annexed the site where the new building was under construction. Speaking for Collins Radio, attorney C. J. Lynch noted that city officials had proposed the annexation, and Collins felt the decision was fair, since the company realized the area would become an integral part of corporate Cedar Rapids. C. W. Garberson, city attorney, pointed out that the city would benefit with many citizens employed at the laboratory, and that its value would provide added tax revenue to the city.

"The attitude of Collins officials with respect to paying for services and taxes has been so fair, and the general type of in-

The site of the new engineering building was directly east (left) of the grove near the intersection of Old Marion Road (horizontal in the middle of the photograph) and C Avenue (upper left to lower right). Collins Road was not yet constructed in 1952. The Collins Main Plant can be seen in the upper right corner.

Arthur Collins turned the first chunk of frozen ground in a ceremony to start construction of the engineering building in January 1953. Pictured from left: C. G. Selzer, J. B. Tuthill, R. S. Gates, Bob Weinhardt, W. H. Bigger, E. D. Broderick, and Collins.

The engineering building under construction.

dustry is so outstanding, that the city should take every step it can to extend the services they need,'' Garberson said.

One feature in the construction was the addition of wire screens in all the concrete walls to keep radio signals from leaving the building. Some residents in the Main Plant neighborhood had complained of interference with their television sets, so Collins took measures to eliminate the problem. Most of the problems at the Main Plant arose when large Voice of America transmitters were tested.

The big move to the new engineering building started in November, 1953, and continued through March, 1954. All

The engineering building was complete and occupied by mid-1954.

major segments of the move were done on weekends, with planners achieving their goal of losing no more than one day's work in each department moved. Working with plant engineer Bill Weinhardt were Walt Brown, who was in charge of moving offices, stock rooms and the library; and Merrill Ludvigson, who supervised the moving of lab facilities. Each weekend vans were at the building at 5:30 p.m. Friday to transport material to the new location. The first day would end at 1:30 a.m. Saturday with the material in its new location and placed in its new space. At 7:30 a.m. Saturday the crews returned to unpack, clean and arrange the material, an operation usually completed by 1:30 p.m. The electrical wiring and telephone service connections were also done on the weekends.

All major departments in the engineering division except one were moved. The moving company, Calder's Van and Storage Company of Cedar Rapids, was the same one which, in 1933, moved Collins Radio into its first factory at 2920

The Collins of Canada building on Bermondsey Road in Toronto.

First Avenue using two small truck loads. Twenty years later, more than 125 vans full of equipment and furnishings changed location — to move just the engineering division.

Construction and moving weren't the only large tasks resulting from the new engineering building. Landscaping received much attention, since the building was to be situated in a natural grove of trees.

First to get the attention of Earl Fredrickson and his grounds maintenance crew were the 181 trees already on site. Thirty-two were stragglers which were removed, along with 13 big trees beyond repair. The other trees required major surgery by the tree service working with Collins maintenance people. Special feeding of the trees worked their roots to the proper level for grading, and every tree was cabled together to prevent limbs from splitting off in windstorms. Grading was difficult because of the many trees, so much of the work was done by hand. In the fall, the crew planted 3,000 pounds of grass seed. Evergreens from all parts of Iowa and Illinois were planted around the entrance of the building. Fredrickson said this was the first full-grown planting of such size in this part of the country. The evergreens weighed up to seven tons and their transportation was a problem in itself.

"No effort was made to rush through the job," Fredrickson said. "We are anxious to do the best possible work, with the results a 52-acre park of which the employees and the city will be proud."

Two subsidiaries formed

Collins Radio Company of Canada was founded in 1953 as a wholly-owned subsidiary of the parent company in Cedar Rapids. An office was established in Ottawa to provide technical assistance to a Canadian manufacturer of Collins-designed equipment, to maintain liaison with the Canadian government and to promote sales of Collins products.

In 1954, the headquarters moved to Toronto and operated from a hotel room for several months to lay the groundwork for production facilities. Collins of Canada leased a building in February, 1955, and production got under way at the new plant the following July. Key product lines in the early history of Collins of Canada were UHF radios for the Canadian government and the DEW Line. With expansion of the original building and the leasing of a second building, total floor space reached 50,000 square feet by 1956. The Toronto plant also housed a research and development lab, Collins-Canada sales headquarters and a field service repair depot.

A second subsidiary was formed in January, 1956, when

The mobile KWM-1 amateur radio is demonstrated by John Hunt in a 1958 Chevrolet.

While Collins Radio's product line diversified, its oldest product line — and the sentimental favorite of veteran Collins employees — was the famous Collins ''ham'' line.

One of the biggest flurries of interest on the amateur radio frequencies since the introduction of amateur single sideband equipment in 1955 was created two years later by the announcement of the KWM-1. This small mobile ham transceiver provided the first opportunity for the mobile operator to benefit from single sideband. Collins engineers studied interior sketches and measurements of a variety of automobiles, then followed up in new car showrooms and in the company's parking lots.

Within the first week of selling, more than 500 orders were taken by telephone, sight unseen, delivery dates and prices undetermined.

When screaming mobs in Venezuela besieged Vice President Richard Nixon and his party in 1958, immediate communication was urgently needed with Washington, D.C. Phone lines leading out of Caracas were completely tied up by the crisis, so Nixon's pilot and longtime ham, Colonel Tommy Collins (no relation to the company) rushed to his hotel room, grabbed a battered suitcase, flipped open the lid and removed a Collins KWM-1 mobile transceiver. Dropping an antenna out his hotel window, the colonel fired up the set and in minutes was in direct contact with the White House through phone patches by American amateur radio operators.

The successor unit to the KWM-1 traveled with many explorers to remote regions of the earth. The best-known explorer to use a KWM-2 was Sir Edmund Hillary, the New Zealander who first conquered the world's highest peak — Mt. Everest. It was during Sir Hillary's 1960 expedition that the Collins KWM-2 transceiver won its stripes as a mountain climber. And more importantly, the equipment played a vital role as a life-saver on the expedition.

Tragedy first struck the expedition above the 20,000-foot level when Peter Mulgrew, the radio operator, began hemorrhaging from the lungs.

His companions slipped and clawed their way back down the mountain with Mulgrew in a make-shift stretcher. It took them three days to reach the 19,000-foot level where the radio was.

Firing up the KWM-2, the explorers raised Katmandu and asked for a helicopter rescue. It took another three days to lower Mulgrew to a point where a helicopter could reach him and fly to a hospital.

Shortly thereafter, Sir Hillary was stricken with a mild heart attack and the expedition again signalled for assistance.

Although both of Mulgrew's legs were amputated because of frostbite, he continued to operate a ham rig during his convalescence — the same set that traveled with him and transmitted the lifesaving message.

In 1959, Collins introduced S-Line, a new line of amateur gear. Advanced circuit design simplified operation, and the line featured compact, functional styling.

The next year, one of the most devastating earthquakes on record ripped through Agadir, Morocco, killing 10,000 inhabitants and injuring more than 35,000 others. First to bring relief was a team of Military Affiliated Radio System (MARS) operators equipped with Collins S-Line. During the four days following the disaster the MARS team provided most of the communication in and out of the stricken city.

Why is Collins ham radio gear the noted leader? There is no single reason. The Collins amateur product line traditionally had the advantage of top engineering talent. Another factor is the company's concern with mechanical and physical design characteristics. The manufacturing and testing procedures which Collins amateur gear goes through is another reason for the equipment's "second to none" rating. A final factor is the sales and distributor forces developed for Collins amateur products.

"Combine all these components," as one sportsminded ham said in 1961 when asked to evaluate Collins amateur equipment, "it's like the New York Yankees, War Admiral and Joe Louis of ham equipment all packed into one box."

Upper
S-Line "ham" units were the neat and attractive radios considered to be top-of-the-line equipment for amateur operators.

Lower
In 1979, the Collins KWM-380 became the first amateur radio introduced by the company since the S-Line units 20 years previously. Dave Berner, amateur products program manager, watched as Al Dorhoffer, editor of CQ magazine, operated the new transceiver.

Collins purchased Communications Accessories Company of Hickman Mills, Missouri (17 miles from Kansas City). The Collins board of directors issued 33,150 shares of Class B (non-voting) common stock for all the stock of the Missouri company and acquired full ownership.

Communication Accessories Co. was founded in 1948, and sales increased steadily from $15,000 its first year to nearly $1 million by 1954. The firm employed 450 persons in three shifts using 20,000 square feet of floor space to manufacture advanced toroidal coils, magnetic amplifiers and filters. Government contractors, who used many of the company's components in missile work, were the largest single customer category, purchasing about 60 percent of the firm's output.

Typical CAC customers included Collins, Western Electric, Western Union, Motorola, Bendix, RCA, Westinghouse, General Electric, Crosley, and Wilcox Electric Company.

Like Collins Radio, the Missouri company was successful because of a significant invention which placed it apart from its competition. The invention was a device that could wind coils on cores extremely rapidly. And also like Collins, CAC was founded by a man who carried through an idea and built a working model.

Ed King constructed his first coil winder in the basement of his father-in-law's grocery store in 1948. King also originated a process to encapsulate toroids in plastic. After the purchase of CAC by Collins in 1956, King remained as president and general manager of the subsidiary until 1959, when he left to form King Radio, which now competes with Collins in the aviation electronics marketplace.

In 1957, CAC moved into its new 57,000 square foot plant at Lee's Summit, Missouri. The 1957 Collins Radio annual report cited the move and a ten-day strike at CAC as major factors which caused a $235,000 loss for the subsidiary that year.

One month after CAC moved to Lee's Summit, a tornado struck Hickman Mills, the former area of operations for the subsidiary and where many CAC employees still lived. No CAC employees were seriously injured, although homes of some were destroyed.

In 1962, the operations of CAC were moved from Lee's Summit to California and combined with the components manufacturing effort at Santa Anna to form the company's Components Division. Certain administrative functions of the new division were combined with those of the Information Science Center at Newport Beach, California. *(See Chapter 8.)*

1956 Fire

A defective oil heater set off a blaze causing a $200,000 loss in two metal buildings at the Cedar Rapids Main Plant February 6, 1956. Originating in one of the Butler buildings used for maintenance and as a garage, the fire destroyed maintenance stock, tools and a new station wagon. In the adjoining components test lab, heat from the fire damaged test equipment and offices.

Within minutes after Howard Batchelder and Floyd Ladman were forced from the burning building, brigade members and other night shift volunteers rushed coatless into the sub-freezing weather to fight the fire. A two-alarm call brought city firemen from five companies. Flames were subdued within a half-hour, but heavy smoke poured out of the buildings for some time.

Prompt action by plant guards, Collins fire brigade personnel, maintenance men and volunteers won the praise of company officials.

Microwave communications

A significant field which unfolded in the early 1950s was the development of microwave communications.

Microwaves are ordinary radio waves, but are extremely small in wavelength. The waves of AM radio broadcasts, for example, are about a quarter of a mile long. Those of microwaves range from two feet down to less than 1/12th of an inch.

Microwaves themselves were not new. The first deliberately-made electromagnetic waves, produced by Heinrich Hertz in 1888, were microwaves. However, during the early days of radio the longer wavelengths were favored because it was difficult to generate large power at microwave wavelengths, and because transmission distances at those frequencies were limited. Beginning with the development of the vacuum tube shortly before World War I, radio made a gradual movement up the frequency spectrum to the shorter wavelengths. During World War II, microwave frequencies achieved much of their fame in radar applications.

Microwave development after the war owed its rapid growth primarily to inherent economies. Although coaxial and other transmission systems could provide similar service and performance, microwave equipment had significant economies in maintenance and operation. It could also provide common carrier remote control and telemetering.

This led to the growth of private industrial communications systems, high speed data transmission and closed-circuit television where the cost of other methods of transmission would have been prohibitive.

Besides offering additional frequency space, microwave transmission allowed many stations to operate on the same frequencies without interference. Microwave frequencies were more easily confined to line-of-sight transmission using antennas which directed the signals in narrow beams.

As early as 1951, Collins Radio Company regarded microwave as a new field of expansion. Previous work at the Collins hangar laboratory in Cedar Rapids showed that the Resnatron could produce high-power microwaves. Microwave studies were transferred to Dallas, where Texas Division engineers studied communication needs of the telephone and pipeline industries. After a year of analysis, Collins management decided to design and manufacture some of the first commercially available microwave equipment.

Two preliminary projects were started: (1) a low power line-of-sight microwave system and (2) a 24-channel carrier system. Collins engineers were satisfied with their early results, so microwave development started in earnest late in

1952. By the spring of 1954 the first prototype was in service between Dallas and Irving, Texas.

Collins sold its first microwave system in 1954 to the California Interstate Telephone Company, and the second sale followed when the company furnished a system to A. J. Hodges Industries, a lumber and oil firm in Shreveport, Louisiana. This system was put into operation in 1955 soon after Collins began mass-producing microwave equipment.

That same year, industry took note of the important advantages of microwave in improving production standards. One of the first of these was recorded when Collins provided a 708-mile communication system between Houston, Texas, and Ponca City, Oklahoma, for the Sinclair and Continental Pipeline Companies. Completed in 1956, the system represented the largest battery-powered, privately-owned microwave system in the world. The project was the first high-density microwave system in the petroleum industry. Al Petrasek, Texas Division sales engineer, negotiated the million-dollar contract.

Deep snow around some microwave relay towers for the Northern Pacific Railway Company meant Collins had to construct two-story buildings to house equipment and provide shelter for communications maintenance teams during storms. 1969 photo.

A variety of microwave radio equipment undergoes final tests in Dallas prior to shipment.

From that point on, Collins achieved several significant milestones in the production of microwave systems. One of its most important programs started in 1956 when the company began preliminary negotiations with the Federal Aviation Administration. The FAA was searching for a more effective method to control and monitor the movement of air traffic, and required radar surveillance coverage throughout the country. Under three contracts totaling about $25 million, Collins Radio provided FAA microwave remoting systems which made up the world's largest communication and radar data handling complex. Forty major air traffic control centers throughout the United States were linked by 95 microwave systems, totaling 631 individual microwave stations spanning more than 16,000 miles.

From its inception, microwave research and development at Collins centered on a basic design philosophy stressing reliability of the equipment. This led to several significant contributions. The most important was pioneering use of a floating battery-powered plant to eliminate disruption of communications by power failures. This principle was used in some of the earliest Collins systems. Another contribution came in 1955 when the company decided to manufacture a carrier multiplex apparatus to be compatible with international standard carriers. This design resulted in the use of a fully synchronous multiplex system using the Collins mechanical filter.

The most significant step in microwave development on an international basis came when Collins developed a large system in Venezuela. In 1958, officials of Compania Shell de Venezuela were given a demonstration of a Collins tropospheric scatter communications system which had been developed for the military services. The South American oil company officials decided to use Collins equipment to connect an oil refinery at Cardon to an oil field at Concepcion near the large city of Maracaibo. The next step came when the oil company decided to extend communications circuits from Caracas 234 miles into Maracaibo. The effort was designed to establish two important business centers with

Microwave relay towers were often located in forbidding terrain, such as this station for a British Columbia hydroelectric company.

107

dependable communication for the first time. Collins engineers were able to connect the two cities by spanning a 7,200-foot ridge with a tropospheric scatter system, and connecting the scatter system to the two cities with microwave links. In May, 1958, the system was turned on, and for the first time 24-hour telephone and teletype service was available between Caracas, Cardon and Maracaibo.

Collins microwave also furnished a high degree of reliability for military applications. Company microwave and carrier systems provided communications for the Atlas Missile Complex at Frances E. Warren Air Force Base at Cheyenne, Wyoming. Collins engineered, furnished and installed equipment for the Pacific Missile Range at Point Mugu, California. Fort Bliss, Texas, one of the world's busiest missile ranges, installed a range safety and communications system using Collins microwave equipment.

One of the first long microwave systems in the United States was constructed for Mid-Valley Pipeline Communication System. This extensive system stretched from Longview, Texas, to Lima, Ohio, and included a master control station at Longview equipped with 26 channel ends of telemetry, supervisory control and alarm, telegraph and voice.

In 1962, Collins provided the microwave equipment for the first statewide educational television network, established in South Carolina. Collins also provided microwave systems and equipment for other large educational television networks. These installations included the Pennsylvania Public Television Network, Kentucky ETV System, Indiana ETV System, Georgia ETV Network, the University of Texas System, the TAGER System in Dallas, and the Louisiana Hospital Video Network.

By the late 1960s, microwave installations completed or in process included systems for railroads, independent and Bell System telephone companies, control of high voltage power conversion and transmission systems, and a regional gas distribution network.

Western Electric emerged as the largest producer of microwave equipment, due to the vast requirements of the Bell Telephone Systems. By the 1960s, Western Electric manufactured virtually all the high density microwave systems needed for multi-channel telephone trunk lines. But Collins Radio succeeded as a major supplier in the medium density microwave market, which included systems capable of handling anywhere from a few dozen to several hundred circuits.

Once again the success of Collins to compete with a much

larger corporation lay in its ability to specialize for a particular segment of the market and to provide top quality products.

Single sideband

Because of inventions and the application of methods such as the Autotune and Class B modulation, Collins Radio became known for developing techniques and designs, and manufacturing components and subsystems as "building blocks" for a variety of end uses. In turn, these resulted in important new segments of business. One of the most significant for Collins during its history was actually not a market segment, but rather a *method* of communication applied to many markets. It was called single sideband modulation.

Simply stated, single sideband is a form of radio frequency modulation (just as AM and FM are forms) in which the normal carrier signal is eliminated and one of the two modulation sidebands is removed by filtering. Single sideband was not invented at Collins, but the company was the first and principal developer of practical single sideband techniques.

The original development of single sideband came about because of certain limitations in radiotelephone circuits. Experiments were first conducted by John R. Carson of the Bell Research and Development Labs, and the American Telephone & Telegraph Company in 1915. In the 1920s, AT&T used single sideband in regular transatlantic telephone communications. The problem was that it took a whole roomful of equipment to generate and filter a single sideband signal.

In the years following the transatlantic phone service, the use of single sideband was limited to wire and low frequency applications. A general lack of interest in conserving spectrum space led to the opening of other portions of the radio frequency spectrum. In addition, early developments in FM transmission led some to believe that FM might be the ultimate form of voice communications.

The advent of World War II brought an unparalleled need for communication facilities. From this necessity, advances in electronics technology came quickly. Major breakthroughs in basic knowledge and manufacturing techniques during and following the war were important factors in development of HF single sideband communication.

Even back in the 1930s, Collins engineers recognized three requirements necessary to make single sideband practical for general communications use: (1) better frequency stability, (2) smaller and lower cost single sideband filters, and (3) better linear amplifiers.

Collins Radio engineers set out to conquer those challenges in the late 1940s. The high frequency portion of the radio spectrum was crowded, and some in the industry thought the congestion threatened to limit the future of high frequency radio. But at Collins, researchers realized the importance of high frequencies that could carry around the world. They looked for a way to make high frequency radio more reliable and efficient by rigidly controlling the sidebands radiated by each transmitter to prevent interference. The engineers also sought a way for receivers to select channels much more precisely with less selective fading.

One of the biggest breakthroughs was introduced by Collins in March, 1952. Announcement of a new device called the mechanical filter was made at the Institute of Radio Engineers' 1952 convention in New York. The principle of mechanical filters had been known for many years, but it took Collins engineers to apply them to radio communications. Mechanical filter development started in Cedar Rapids and was transferred to Burbank.

The mechanical filter made possible better control of transmitter sideband radiation and receiver selectivity, so it simplified single sideband communication. The advantages of the small size and increased selectivity of the mechanical filter made it natural for application to common radio problems. The first application was in the Collins 75A-2 amateur receiver. This set was offered with one or more of the filters, depending on the number of selectivity curves the operator wanted.

But these were the Cold War years after the Korean conflict, and most technology advancements were quickly recruited for the military. The United States had bombers in the air on a 24-hour basis, ready for any threat of war. Radio technology had not kept pace with the rapid advances of aviation, and the long-range radios aboard high flying jets often could not communicate with Air Force ground stations.

Armed with the capabilities of the mechanical filter, the previously developed permeability-tuned oscillator and linear tuned circuits a Collins engineering group organized in November, 1952, to investigate single sideband techniques and to develop prototype equipment. The work, under the personal direction of Arthur Collins, took place in the Butler buildings south of the Main Plant in Cedar Rapids. Among the engineers who made significant contributions were Robert Miedke, Vince DeLong, Dale McCoy, William Perkins, Kenneth Rigoni, John Sherwood, Richard Uhrik, Walter Zarris, and Warren Bruene. E. W. Pappenfus was chief engineer for Collins single sideband development activity.

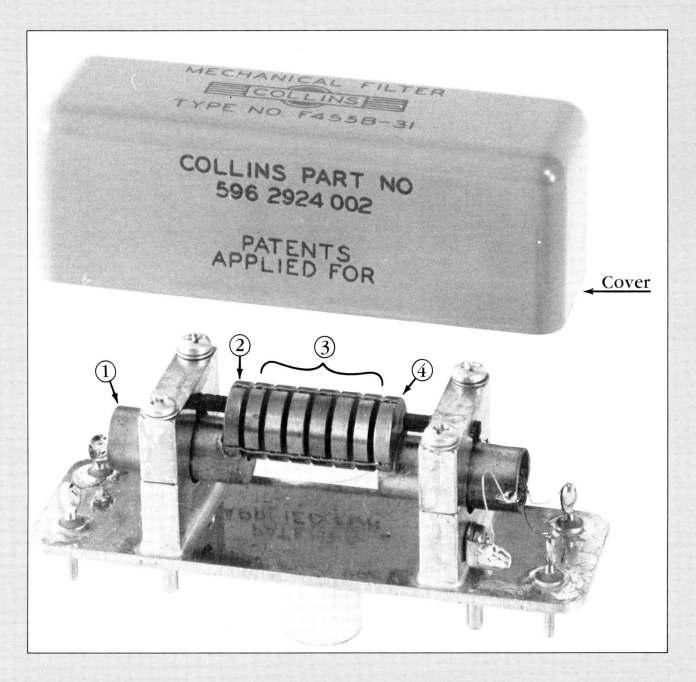

The mechanical filter uses the principle of the tuning fork, taught in high school physics. When struck, the tuning fork sounds a fixed tone in perfect pitch. It also vibrates at its precise tone when a like sound impinges upon it. Collins engineers saw this principle as a way of filtering out different frequency radio signals.

They made a stack of small metal discs, each with a precise resonance frequency, spaced along wires. When electrical impulses are applied to an electromagnet at the input end of the filter (1), the first disc (2) vibrates to the desired signal. Then each disc down the line (3) carries this signal and helps purify the signal by weeding out other vibrations.

The last disc (4) feeds the sorted signal into the main circuit of the receiver. This amounts to a translation of an electrical signal into mechanical force, then translation back into electricity after filtering.

Besides being efficient from an engineer's viewpoint, the mechanical filter performed the job at less cost than other devices could at the time.

The hours of intense study concluded when a course of product development was established.

In 1952, Arthur Collins predicted 28,000-channel radios would be used on aircraft, because of the new single sideband techniques. The proposed radios for swift aircraft would have power ten times that of the telegraphy radios then in use.

In April, 1953, Robert Mitchell led a group assigned to develop a single sideband exciter and transmitter for the government. That September, Dave Weber headed a group to develop an advanced communications receiver for general commercial use with single sideband techniques.

General Curtis LeMay, commander of the U.S. Air Force Strategic Air Command and himself a ham radio operator, was aware of Collins Radio's progress in single sideband. In 1955, Collins was selected by the Air Force to develop, test, and install a complete single sideband air-ground and point-to-point communication system. The project was known as "Birdcall." During work on this project, Collins developed techniques in 50-kilowatt antenna switching, steerable beam antennas, and complete remote control of variable equipment functions from a centralized operating point.

Arthur Collins operates single sideband radio gear in a demonstration for Gen. Curtis LeMay. 1956 photo.

Collins unveiled its achievements in single sideband research and development at the 1957 national convention of the Institute of Radio Engineers in New York. The amateur section of the booth (pictured) attracted many visitors to the KWS-1, 75A-4 and the new KWM-1.

In long-range flights to the North Polar region, the Far East, and Europe and Africa during the next two years, the Strategic Air Command, Collins Radio, and amateur radio operators all over the world demonstrated the effectiveness of

"COLLINS FLIGHT TEST," "AF3X," "RASPUTIN," "LIBERTY," "KHT," "ROCKWELL FLIGHT TEST," — these past and present call names belong to a unique communications facility operated within the Collins Telecommunications Products Division in Cedar Rapids. Most employees know the station as "Comm Central."

Comm Central was built in 1958 in an area of Building 120 known as Lab 12. The Lab 12 station was used to research high frequency communications in conjunction with the military Short Order Program. A display and observation booth were built around the station to showcase the developments of Collins Radio.

An interim station was built and operated in the Short Order Net from 1960 until the Communications and Data System Division designed and built a complete communications system.

In 1962, the station that many remember as "Liberty" was opened and operated from the new communications and data building (Building 121). The operators called the station the "fish bowl" because of the glass walls.

The Cedar Rapids station became known as "Liberty" during the 1960s when Communications Central was involved with the Andrews VIP network. Collins had a contract with the Air Force to serve as either the primary communication station or as a backup whenever Air Force One, the presidential aircraft, and other aircraft in the VIP fleet carried cabinet members or high-ranking military officers. Over the airwaves the station's call word was "Liberty."

During the Vietnam war years, Comm Central was active in the Military Affiliated Radio System (MARS). During 1967 alone, Comm Central completed 7,122 patches from servicemen in Vietnam to friends and loved ones all across the country.

Comm Central was also involved in many special communication projects. One such project — the Rockwell polar flight, which took place in November, 1965 — was the first around-the-world flight to pass over both the North and South poles. The Boeing 707 established eight world records for jet transports and the crew conducted many scientific experiments. One of the 40 persons on board was Lowell Thomas, Jr. Thomas fed regular voice reports of the flight to Comm Central where they were relayed to Lowell Thomas, Sr., at the CBS studio in New York for his nightly news program. Aboard the aircraft, Collins provided long-range communication with a 618T-2 transceiver. The purpose of the Collins experiment was to obtain data on high frequency propagation conditions from many locations over a short period of time.

An engineering assistant in Collins' propagation research, John Demuth, was aboard the aircraft to serve as radio operator. At no time throughout the three-day flight were they unable to make contact between the aircraft and the ground station, even from the normally difficult propagation areas surrounding the poles. *(Editor's note: The navigator on the Rockwell polar flight, Loren DeGroot, joined Collins in 1972.)*

Two other 1966 around-the-world business jet flights also were supported by the Liberty station. They were the Learjet flight which established 20 world speed records, and the Rockwell-Standard Aero Commander flight which included Arthur Godfrey as one of its crewmen. A Collins 618T single side-band transceiver was bolted into the luggage rack of the Learjet, and a 26-foot wire was used as an antenna. Over 97 percent communications reliability was achieved around the world on both flights.

An Amelia Earhart commemorative flight by aviator Ann Pelegrino in 1968 was another globe-girdling mission for which the Liberty station provided nearly 100 percent communications reliability.

Plaisted polar expedition

The Plaisted expedition, which used motorized snow sleds to cross the Arctic to the North Pole in 1967 and 1968, also maintained communications with home via Comm Central.

The overland trip to the North Pole started out as a dream conceived by Ralph Plaisted and Dr. Arthur Aufderheide to launch the first surface assault on the North Pole in 58 years.

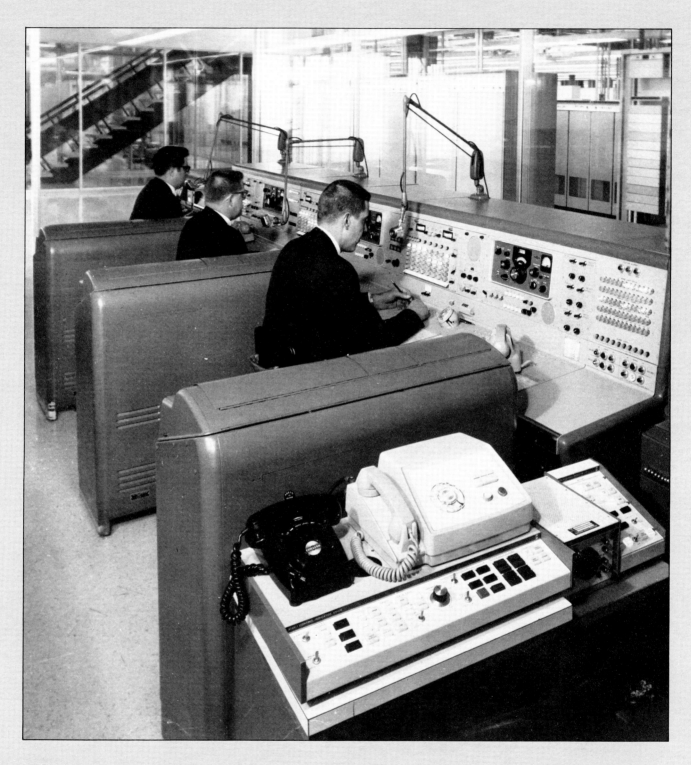

Although their first attempt in 1967 failed, the team of ten Americans and Canadians tried again the next year and reached its destination on April 19, 1968.

It was with Collins communications equipment that the world learned of the achievement. The equipment was used for communica-

tions between the ice party and base camp, base camp and Comm Central, and the ice party and Comm Central. Reports from the ice party dealt with ice conditions, progress made, condition of the men, requests for supply drops, and personal messages.

Plaisted said the Collins transceivers functioned well even though

Comm Central was located in Building 121 in the 1960s. Pictured from left are Bill Ahrens, Ron Wilson and Heinz Blankenhagen. In the foreground is secure voice encryption equipment used with Air Force I communications. Large 45-kilowatt transmitters can be seen through the glass panels.

they were subjected to a severe beating over the "most miserable ice anyone could imagine."

Don Powellek, who operated the KWM-2s on the ice and back at base camp, said, "The reliability is way beyond our expectations. We were able to communicate at any time we chose, either to Cedar Rapids or other parts of the world. We have made some fabulous contacts."

First word that Plaisted had reached the pole came through the Collins Comm Central. Charles Kuralt of CBS News was present to talk with Plaisted. The interview was viewed by millions of Americans who watched the Saturday evening news program the following night.

Manhattan project

In the fall of 1969, Collins equipment aboard a huge ice-breaking oil tanker played an important role in a $26 million gamble.

In a dramatic attempt to open the long-sought Northwest Passage through Arctic seas, two United States oil companies and a British firm combined efforts to establish a sea route to rich oil fields discovered at Alaska's Prudhoe Bay. If Arctic oil could be shipped in quantity through the ice-choked waters, the eastern United States would gain access to a vast new fuel supply. The decision by Humble Oil and Refining, Atlantic Richfield and British Petroleum to challenge the Northwest Passage captured the admiration of Arctic experts, but many were skeptical of the chances for the mission's success.

Because of the high priority given to communications and the urgent need to have the system installed, Humble asked Collins Radio to satisfy all the communications requirements of the expedition and put the system in working order within 60 days. The high frequency single sideband equipment installed included a ship-board communications system, amateur radios, a log periodic antenna and a vertical antenna. The *Manhattan* was the first known commercial vessel to use a log periodic antenna. Tanker-based helicopters were equipped by Collins with homing systems, automatic direction finders and two separate VHF transceivers to

allow them to find a hand-held radio beacon used by landing parties. Small VHF radios were supplied by Collins for use by landing parties.

More communications message traffic was handled on the *Manhattan's* three-month voyage than most ships conduct during a lifetime. During its first month at sea, the *Manhattan* averaged 7 hours, 20 minutes of communications traffic per day. The ship made more than 5,000 logged contacts with Comm Central's maritime station, KHT, while at sea, plus additional contacts with commercial carriers handling short-wave radio traffic in the Arctic. About one-fourth of the contacts with KHT were via 100-word-per-minute radio-teletype.

Throughout its journey the *Manhattan* maintained 96 percent communications reliability between the ship and the Liberty station, despite such factors as solar flares and magnetic storms. Messages sent from the *Manhattan* were picked up by the Liberty station in Cedar Rapids and relayed to Humble headquarters by way of direct telephone lines.

Flying grandfather

Max Conrad, the famous "Flying Grandfather," departed Winona, Min-

To find a new route for shipping oil from Alaska, the USS Manhattan broke through frozen Arctic waters. Comm Central handled communications for the voyage in 1969.

nesota, on November 30, 1969, on a trip around the world over the poles. This was his second attempt in a twin-engine Piper Aztec named the "St. Louis Woman." Comm Central provided communications for the flight using several calls on high frequency networks. Conrad's aircraft was equipped with a Collins 618T transceiver.

First 747 to London
A single sideband link to the Liberty station in 1970 enabled Americans to witness, through radio network broadcasts, a historic new era of aviation — the first regular service flight of Pan American World Airways' giant Boeing 747 jet from New York to London.

Radio network correspondents aboard the new aircraft gave accounts of the flight. Reports came live via Collins single sideband high frequency radio from the aircraft to the Liberty station, and were fed into landlines to network headquarters in New York.

The 747 inaugural service flight was not the first in which the Liberty station maintained radio contact with a 747 across the Atlantic. When one of the transports was flown from the Boeing plant near Seattle, Washington, non-stop to the 1969 Paris air show, the Collins communications link was utilized for position and progress reports.

The new look
After spending the last ten years of its colorful 25-year history under a stairwell in Building 121, Comm Central was moved and redesigned in 1983 to keep pace with the changing high frequency communications market. Yellow tablets and dial pulse control were replaced by computer terminals and printers. Integrated into the design of the new. communications complex was a section dedicated to historical achievements by the various Collins divisions.

The new station features four communication consoles, two mainframe computer systems, a solid-state antenna matrix, and the Collins line of HF-80 communications equipment. A remote-controlled station in Newport Beach is controlled by the station in Cedar Rapids via computer.

Comm Central is licensed as an experimental high frequency research station, an aeronautical flight test station, and as a limited coast maritime station. The radio traffic handled by the station includes communication and phone patching to aircraft, drill rigs, and tankers on the high seas. Comm Central is also involved in marketing demonstrations for customers, and serves as a display area for Collins high frequency products.

Nine operators keep the station manned 24 hours a day, seven days a week. The operators, under the supervision of Heinz Blankenhagen, are: Jack Bond, Lewis Darrah, Justin Dennis, Joe Dzikonski, Ike Hand, Leonard Peters, Rick Plummer, Floyd (Robbie) Robinson, and Ty Smith.

In the early 1970s, Comm Central moved to a secluded area in Building 121. Radio operator pictured is Joe Dzikonski. In 1983, a new home was constructed for the facility, including a visitor's viewing area.

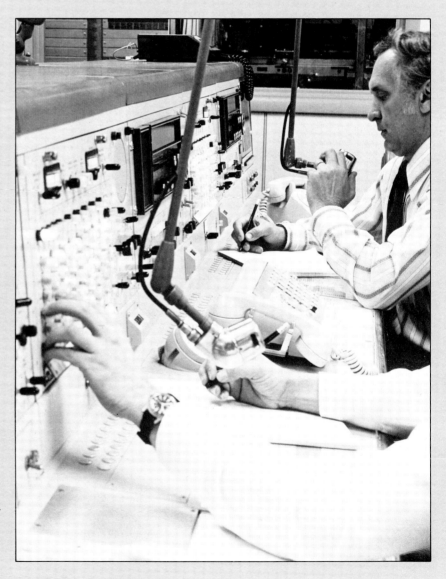

116

single sideband in global communication. In flights of an Air Force C97, the airborne station worked all continents and maintained continuous contact with a ham network in the United States.

The equipment — standard Collins single sideband ham gear — was installed in the passenger compartment of the C97 airplane. Operators included General F. H. Griswold, vice commander of the Strategic Air Command; and Arthur Collins, company president.

One of the high points of the experiment was establishing direct interpolar communication between the North and South Poles. Interpolar contact was maintained at regular intervals for three hours one night and for seven hours the following night in July, 1956. Overall results of the flights were outstanding. The airplane maintained virtually 100 percent communication with every sideband-equipped ham contacted.

In 1957, Collins again demonstrated the advantages of single sideband during the first non-stop, around-the-world flight of three of the Air Force's new B-52 bombers. Modified Collins KWS-1 transmitters and 75A-4 receivers were used as the ground stations on the project.

High frequency single sideband proved itself to the Air Force, providing a spectrum saving of one-half the space ordinarily employed, a nine-to-one improvement in talking power, and immunity to selective fading in the polar regions.

The Short Order Program, a Strategic Air Command communications network project which began in 1958, was based on the operating philosophies which evolved in the Birdcall Project.

"We can now make instant contact with any of our more than 2,000 bombers whether they are at the North Pole or South," said General Griswold in 1960. Short Order, designed and installed by Collins and its systems subsidiary, Alpha Corporation *(see accompanying story),* used single sideband high frequency radio equipment and a vast array of control and switching gear to provide a system that operated automatically under the simple control of an ordinary telephone dial. The system consisted of four stations, all located in the United States. If one of the stations failed to reach a far-reaching aircraft because of propagation difficulties, one or all three other stations were used by remote control via four-wire telephone landlines which connected the stations. Equipment for Short Order was designed, developed and manufactured by the three Collins divisions: Cedar Rapids, Texas and Western, with Alpha Corporation providing system design, management and installation.

Three stories underground at the headquarters of the Strategic Air Command, a controller speaks with aircraft over the "Short Order" radio communication system engineered by the Alpha Corporation, systems management subsidiary of Collins Radio. 1961 photo.

By the late 1950s, the size and complexity of electronics installations had increased to such proportions that the most practical way to deal with the problem, as Collins saw it, was through a systems concept. Worldwide systems engineering requirements led to the formation of a new Collins subsidiary — Alpha Corporation.

Incorporated in Texas in 1959, Alpha Corporation extended Collins' activities for the detailed management of space age technical projects, both in the United States and abroad. Headquartered in Richardson, Texas, the company was staffed to design, construct, and install complex government and commercial systems. This included not only each electronic system involved, but also the complete "turnkey" installations with buildings, roads, towers — everything down to the washroom and the lock on the door. After installation, Alpha provided training for customer engineers and technicians assigned to the installation, or furnished complete crews of skilled specialists to staff the finished projects.

Max Burrell, a vice president for the parent company, was made president of Alpha Corporation. John Nyquist was vice president and general manager. Other officers also performed double duty as Alpha and Collins managers.

Although Alpha was established to function as a completely independent entity, program managers drew on the research and manufacturing capabilities of the parent company, and also integrated specialized equipment from other manufacturers into systems when needed.

One of the biggest contracts for Alpha was the Strategic Air Command's "Short Order" communications network. This system consisted of four single sideband ground stations in widely separated sections of the United States. Alpha also did important work for the Pacific Missile Range, and tactical data and multipurpose communications systems for the U.S. Navy.

In 1961, Alpha Corporation was changed from a subsidiary to a division within Collins Radio Company. The following year, Alpha Division and the Texas Division were merged to form the Dallas Division.

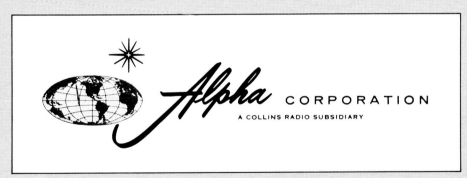

But the Collins achievements did more than produce an Air Force contract. Single sideband revolutionized high frequency communications. The company initiated extensive propagation studies to gain more knowledge about single sideband capabilities. Single sideband was soon the standard for civil aviation long-range communication and for a host of other military and commercial applications.

By 1960, single sideband products supplanted aviation electronics as the largest segment of business at Collins Radio, even though single sideband was more accurately a type of communication rather than a classification of business. For example, there was overlapping of the aviation electronics field with that of single sideband, because the transceivers supplied to the Air Force were also used by the overseas airlines.

Antennas — the ears and voice of radio

Just as the human voice creates pressure waves in the air which the ears detect, antennas play a similar role in radio communication. Antennas are the vital link between signal generating and receiving devices and space, which is the medium that supports radio wave communication. Collins Radio has long recognized the important role the antenna plays in high quality communications systems, and backed this recognition with large investments in equipment and company-sponsored research and development.

In the early days of the company, antenna research personnel numbered so few they did not have a formal group in the Collins organization. Nevertheless, they did have a laboratory — an uninsulated wooden building near the Main Plant in Cedar Rapids during World War II called Fort Dearborn *(See Chapter 3)*. Antenna engineers increased in number to comprise two large departments by the mid-1960s. From the beginning, the goal of antenna research at Collins was to provide a high-quality, broad-based antenna research and development capability in support and expansion of Collins products. With that goal, the antenna group produced achievements which made it recognized as second to none in the industry.

Aircraft antennas illustrate in the purest sense the successful development of a component in support of a complete airborne electronic system. The "deerhorn" antenna was one such development.

Next was evolution of the first airborne antenna to combine communication and navigation functions in a single unit. The sleek, aerodynamic styling of the 137X-1 earned an award in a design competition in 1959.

119

Hundreds of model log periodic antennas were constructed in the Collins model shop. 1959 photo.

Special support towers held and rotated aircraft models for measurements on antennas mounted on the model aircraft. The height provided a free space effect. 1959 photo.

Left
The "billboard" antenna was the first erected north of the engineering building at a site which came to be called the "antenna farm."

Other airborne antennas developed by Collins included antennas for the U.S. Army's AN/ARC-54 airborne FM transceiver. The ARC-54 communication antenna was a 54-inch "whip" mounted on top of a coupler which was remotely operated by the frequency dial on the pilot's communication console.

Many high frequency antenna designs were developed at Collins during the 1950s. A basic change was made in high frequency antenna design philosophy to go from narrow-band dipole antennas and rhombic antennas to a basic broadband concept, such as the broadband dipole, the discone, the sleeve, and log-periodic antennas. Directional antennas came into wide use, and most were log periodic.

The first antenna built north of the engineering building on the "antenna farm" was called the "billboard." This antenna, which is still in use, is made up of seven 120-foot towers arranged in a circle. By selecting a particular radiating tower across from its corresponding reflecting screen, the operator can choose the direction of coverage for his radio signal.

The second antenna installed at the antenna farm was called a logarithmically periodic antenna. The log periodic antenna principle was discovered by Dr. R. H. DuHamel, head of the Collins antenna group in the 1950s. It was called "one of the most significant antenna design advancements in recent years." Previously, high frequency radios required several antennas to operate over the full frequency range. The log periodic antenna meant a radio could be tuned through a much larger frequency range without changing antennas. The first log periodic antenna at the antenna farm was later replaced with another having an even greater frequency range.

Another example of how Collins' research resulted in benefits for the company as well as national defense is illustrated by the company's "hard" antenna development and production. A hard antenna is one that is designed to survive effects of nuclear weapons. In 1958, Collins recognized the need for a hard antenna for secure communication sites and in communication between hardened missile complexes. Collins built a retractable telescoping antenna which could be raised to a height of 76 feet. The antenna was used in Civil Defense and similar installations. The experience led to development of antennas for Atlas and Titan hardened inter-site communications.

In 1959, the antenna research group was called on to design a transportable reflector antenna. Collins was first to develop an inflatable reflector antenna which could survive

121

the outside environment without the protection of an external radome. It was found that inflatable reflectors as large as 15 feet in diameter could be designed for on-sight erection. The techniques developed by Collins have since been followed by many companies in diverse applications.

For scatter communication terminals with smaller power requirements, Collins developed a 10-foot diameter solid surface reflector. Two of the antennas could be unpacked and erected by four men in two hours.

The ability of Collins to meet communication needs with innovative antenna designs played no small role in Collins Radio's entry, and the entry of the United States, into the space age.

This is one of the tropospheric scatter communications systems Collins provided for the U.S. Army. The system operated by scattering radio energy off the troposphere.

A contest for Collins Radio employees which began in the summer of 1956, was held for the last time in the summer of 1957.

In the 1950s, it was company policy to shut down operations for two weeks in the middle of the summer for inventory, so nearly all employees took their vacations at the same time. This created an exodus from Cedar Rapids and other Collins locations, and, incidentally, caused an annual business slump for local retail stores.

Before the annual shutdown in 1956, it was announced that a $25 cash prize would be awarded to the two employees who had a chance meeting at the most distant point from their plant. So employees could spot each other on the highways and in parking lots, all were issued bumper stickers which read, "Hi, I'm from Collins." To verify the meetings, the two employees were required to write a brief account of their meeting in a letter or on a postcard and mail it from the post office nearest their meeting place to the *Collins Column* office in Cedar Rapids.

Everything seemed to go smoothly in 1956. Hundreds of cards were received, and Ken Johnson of Cedar Rapids was declared the winner for his meeting with Doug Johnson of the New York sales office in Caracas, Venezuela. Doug Johnson was disqualified because he was in Caracas on Collins business and not on vacation.

Organizers of the contest were pleased with the results, so they decided to hold it again in 1957. Joe Franey and Leo Voss each were awarded $25 for their chance meeting in North Vancouver, British Columbia.

At first it looked as though the prize money might go to four employees of the Western Division in Burbank. The first cards received from Robert Bryson and Bill Richardson were postmarked Fairbanks, Alaska, and stated that Bryson met Richardson when his helicopter crashed near a gold mine where Richardson was prospecting. The next cards received were from Davos, Switzerland, and claimed that Jim McPherson was operating a cable car at a ski resort when he ran across Bryson and Richardson. Then came notice of a meeting of McPherson and Bob Postal at a Key West, Florida beach, followed by cards postmarked from Nicaragua, where Bryson said he met Richardson as they were both fishing for fresh water sharks in Lake Nicaragua. And finally the meeting to end all meetings — two postcards arrived from Capetown, South Africa, where Richardson said he ran a canoe into the side of an auto ferry, only to be rescued by the ferry captain, who just happened to be Bryson.

When the "world travelers" were investigated by the Western Division industrial relations department, they had only one question, "Does someone have a sense of humor, or are we all fired?"

Apparently someone had a sense of humor, because there was no indication in the *Collins Column* that they were dismissed.

7

The space age

The quarter-century point in the company's history coincided with a significant transition in the operations of the entire electronics industry.

The rapidly growing scope of commercial applications and military and scientific missions to be performed involved increased complexity, uncompromised reliability and exacting performance. From the 1930s through the early 1950s, units such as high frequency transmitters, the Autotune, and the ARC-27 UHF transceiver were individual units developed to meet individual needs of the industry. But by the late 1950s, this traditional approach of product development was becoming obsolete. Particularly in the military field, complete systems which could perform many functions were necessary. These tasks frequently required the cooperative efforts of a group of companies, both large and small, working under the direction of a systems management contractor. The space programs at Collins were typical of such cooperative efforts.

Early programs in radio astronomy, including use of the moon as a passive relay for communication, development of the radio sextant, and the deep space radio telescope at Anacostia, D.C., gave Collins a strong background in the emerging field of space technology. At the start of the U.S. space program, Collins had perhaps as much knowledge as any company in space communication.

North American Aviation built the first of three X-15 rocket planes in 1957, and Collins Radio received a contract for the communication/navigation system in November of that year. The equipment was delivered in August, 1958, and consisted of elements derived from Collins' standard communications, navigation and identification (CNI) package which it had developed for military jets. Development of the X-15 communication/navigation system was the first venture for Collins, and the United States, in manned space flight.

A sleek, panatela-shaped craft more like a piloted missile than an aircraft, the X-15 was 50 feet long and had thin wings spanning only 22 feet. It was carried aloft to about 40,000 feet and then launched from its B-52 mothership like a fledg-

Saturn V and Apollo spacecraft being assembled at Cape Kennedy. Collins supplied complete communications and tracking systems for the Apollo missions.

125

Dropped from the wing of a B-52, the X-15 used rocket power to accelerate to speeds of more than 3,600 miles per hour.

ling.

The brief experimental flights in which a test pilot soared to the edge of space made significant contributions to America's aeronautics and space knowledge.

Collins' experience in ground systems began in 1958 when the company installed the first NASA Deep Space Instrumentation Facility at Goldstone, California. Successful completion of this station to provide tracking and communication with a deep space vehicle led to contracts for installation of overseas stations at Woomera, Australia, and Johannesburg, South Africa.

Between 1958 and 1963, Collins provided a total of 11 space tracking stations. First of these was at the 85-foot dish antenna facility of the Jet Propulsion Laboratory at Goldstone, California, which was used in many of America's deep space satellite probes. Collins supplied all major equipment except the reflector, mount and hydraulic servo mechanism.

Parallel with this effort was the design and installation of a down-range station in Puerto Rico for tracking the initial trajectory of space probes. The overall technical and management capability, which was essential for programs of this magnitude, did not go unnoticed and led to several additional Collins contracts for the Department of Defense and NASA. One of these required that Collins provide two highly versatile tracking and data acquisition systems to the Defense Department for classified programs. These systems tested Collins' ability to do a "turnkey" job. Portions of a satellite tracking facility were provided for the Electronics Proving Ground at Ft. Hauchuca, Arizona, and six data acquisition facilities for the Goddard Space Flight Center were installed by Collins, beginning in 1962.

An early NASA program to advance the study of space communications was Project Echo. To encourage a great deal of scientific research, NASA invited the radio industry at large to participate in the project on a voluntary basis.

Following the announcement of the project, Collins and its systems subsidiary, Alpha Corporation, actively joined with others in the industry to plan maximum use of the Echo satellites for research. Collins/Alpha participants wanted to test tracking techniques to see if satellite links could be used for speech and teletype transmission.

On August 12, 1960, NASA launched Echo I to study the use of passive communication reflectors. When it reached the prescribed altitude, the metal sphere housing the payload

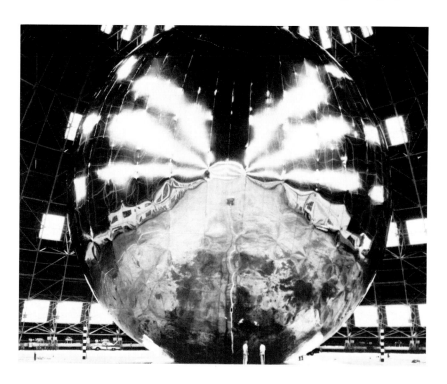

Echo I balloon satellite was test inflated on the ground. NASA photograph.

separated from the rocket. Bursting like a jack-in-the-box from the divided sphere, hundreds of yards of aluminized Mylar plastic poured out. Inside the uninflated plastic balloon was a residue of ten pounds of powdered benzoic acid. On contact with the thin atmosphere, the limp plastic inflated in a matter of seconds to a firmly rounded, gleaming sphere 100 feet in diameter.

The Collins Project Echo tracking station was located northeast of Cedar Rapids.

The following day as the satellite rose over the northwest horizon in its eleventh orbit, Collins tracking antennas in Cedar Rapids and Richardson locked on to their target. In Texas, Al Richmond, project engineer for Alpha, spoke into a microphone: "This is KK2X1C in Richardson, calling KA2XDV in Cedar Rapids, Iowa. Do you read me, Cedar Rapids?" The answer came from Cliff Beamer, Collins research scientist: "This is KA2XDV in Cedar Rapids, Iowa, calling KK2X1C in Richardson, Texas. We receive you loud and clear."

The Collins tracking crew in Cedar Rapids manned the control console during pre-dawn hours as Echo II was launched at Cape Canaveral. Seated from front to rear are Floyd Perkins, Estel Darland and Frank Metecek. Standing are engineers Clifford Beamer (foreground) and Gerald Bergemann.

The first two-way radio voice transmission via artifical satellite had been accomplished.

The following week, on August 19, 1960, Collins research teams achieved another first. Working with photo transmitting equipment supplied by the Associated Press, a wirephoto of President Eisenhower, taken the previous day in Washington, was transmitted by Echo satellite from Cedar Rapids to Richardson. This was the first photograph transmitted by satellite.

In January, 1962, Echo II was launched but met an untimely end. It inflated too rapidly at an altitude of 200 miles,

The first photograph transmitted via satellite was a picture of President Eisenhower, sent from Cedar Rapids to Richardson in 1960.

and the 135-foot balloon exploded into shreds.

The shattered balloon altered, but did not cancel, the plans of Collins engineers and technicians assembled in the company's space tracking station at Cedar Rapids. The Collins crew was able to track and bounce signals from the fragments of the Echo II sphere and received radio signals of "relatively good quality."

The most conspicuous equipment used in the Project Echo experiments were the antennas. Three 28-foot parabolics were installed; one receiving and one transmitting antenna at the tracking station near Cedar Rapids, and the other, a transmitting antenna at the tracking site in Richardson.

Another example of ground tracking experience was Collins' installation of communication, range instrumentation and data handling facilities for the Pacific Missile Range. The range was located throughout the length and breadth of the Pacific Ocean to support firings of tactical, intermediate-range and intercontinental ballistic missiles, and testing of anti-missile missiles, satellites and space reconnaissance vehicles. Collins and Alpha implemented the communication, range instrumentation and data handling facilities at sites within the continental United States, downrange islands and on range instrumentation ships. High frequency single sideband equipment was furnished by Collins for use both ashore and afloat on range vessels. Every major segment of the Collins organization — Cedar Rapids, Burbank, Dallas and Toronto — made significant contributions to the individual equipment or complete systems for the Pacific Missile Range.

Project Mercury

In 1958, after intense competition with other companies, Collins won the prime contract covering onboard communications equipment for the Mercury manned spaceflight program. As a subcontractor to McDonnell Aircraft Corporation, Collins functioned as a systems manager with sole responsibility for the development, delivery, and satisfactory performance of all subsystem components. The Mercury capsule communication system consisted of 30 components produced during two years of developmental work by Collins and its team of subcontractors. Areas of research included: the functional circuits needed for the several phases of communication; the general problem of signal propagation; several special problem areas in manned-capsule electronics, and each piece of major equipment needed to serve the functions of the capsule system.

129

The Mercury communications system included several parts:

Voice Communication. The astronaut and ground personnel had to be able to talk to each other during all phases of the mission. Redundant equipment was used at first to provide a backup for both flight and rescue operations.

Command Function. Redundant command receivers with many on-and-off channels were provided to control various functions within the capsule during the launch, flight and re-entry.

Telemetry. Two telemetry transmitters relayed scientific, operational and aeromedical data from the capsule to the ground.

Precision Tracking. Two radar transponder beacons in the microwave frequency range were used for precision tracking during flight.

Rescue Beacons. Two rescue beacons, operating on international distress frequencies, helped to determine the capsule's bearings during retrieval operations at sea.

M. Scott Carpenter, one of six astronauts to fly a Mercury mission, visited Collins facilities in Cedar Rapids before the

A full-scale mockup of the Mercury capsule was used to test antenna designs. The Collins engineering team responsible for Project Mercury antennas, from left: Dick Hodges, Paul Zimmerman, Ramsey Decker, Tom Mortimore, Mardis Anderson, George Haines, Jim Shure and Leo Griffee. 1959 photo.

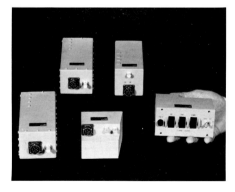

Collins equipment for the Mercury capsule included, from left: high frequency voice transceiver and backup unit, UHF voice power amplifier, UHF rescue voice transceiver, control panel.

first flight and spoke to employees about their role in the space program.

"Every military person who has had anything to do with an operation of any magnitude is aware of the importance of complete communication. I can't think of any one single factor more important. Loss of communication could mean loss of life and loss of national prestige," Carpenter said.

The Mercury communication project team at Collins, headed by Robert Olson and Eugene Habeger, knew that failure of communication electronics in the manned capsule would endanger the astronaut and the mission. The Collins team, along with consultants from Aeronautical Radio, Inc., developed a comprehensive reliability program for the Collins effort, as well as its subcontractors.

The entire first Mercury flight in the spring of 1961 — liftoff to downrange Atlantic return — took just under 16 minutes. The capsule with Captain Alan B. Shepard, Jr., aboard returned safely home. Months of work, study and practice culminated in America's fastest and highest manned flight to date. Shepard's mission was followed by those of Mercury astronauts Grissom, Glenn, Carpenter, Schirra and Cooper.

Collins generated positive publicity during the Mercury

missions by boasting that it was one of the first companies to have some of its equipment actually removed from a program. In each of the first five Mercury flights, two Collins sets were carried: a primary system and a backup system. Before the sixth Mercury mission, flown by Gordon Cooper, the backup systems were removed. The record of the previous flights had been so successful that it was deemed safe to rely on one set and use the weight saved to carry other equipment. Collins project team members were elated.

Experience in the one-man-Mercury spacecraft program led to Collins Radio's participation in Gemini — designing and manufacturing the voice communication system which

During Astronaut Edward White's historic space walk, his voice was transmitted to Earth via Collins equipment.

For the Gemini two-man missions, the Collins voice communications control unit was located directly in front of the astronaut seated on the right (horizontal switches at the bottom of the vertical portion of the panel). McDonnell photo.

performed successfully on all ten of the two-man Gemini missions.

Tragedy caused Apollo design change

Before the last of the Mercury flights, and before the Gemini flights began, plans were launched for the Apollo moon landing program. In December, 1961, it was announced that Collins would supply the complete communications system for the Apollo three-man space missions. The project was described as man's boldest and most extensive program, and one of the most monumental precision jobs in industrial history.

Collins employees designed, developed and manufactured communication and data subsystems used in 22 Apollo command capsules. Most of those modules actually served in space; the rest were used for testing and display.

"Dates were terribly important," said James Westcot, who was Collins' director of business administration on Project Apollo. "North American Aviation (the prime contractor) had an incentive payment program for us if we shipped on time — it was sizable. Overtime didn't mean much. It was getting everything done perfect and shipped on time that counted."

In 1964, more than 500 employees working on Project Apollo received a first-hand challenge to provide "defect free" equipment. The challenge came from astronaut Edward H. White II.

"Unless you do your job, I am not going to be able to do my job," White told workers gathered in the Collins cafeteria.

133

Collins employees who talked with White were shocked and saddened three years later when a fire fed by pure oxygen flared through an Apollo capsule being tested on its launch pad at Cape Kennedy. White, Virgil Grissom, and Roger Chaffee, the team of astronauts slated to make the first

The deaths of astronauts Grissom, Chaffee and White led to design changes for many Apollo systems, including Collins communications equipment.

lunar landing, died in the fire. Critics of America's space program emerged in full cry, and all phases of Project Apollo came under intense scrutiny.

The fire and subsequent investigation brought policy changes at NASA, and had a major impact on Collins' portion of the project. Before the accident, NASA specified the spacecraft equipment be designed so astronauts could perform inflight maintenance. For Collins, this meant all communications equipment had to be modular in construction. Therefore, if a fault occurred, the faulty component could be pulled and replaced. Following the fire, NASA abandoned the inflight maintenance policy and asked for a complete redesign from Collins for its portion of the spacecraft equipment. The original design became known as Block I, and Collins' new design was called Block II. Instead of using modular construction, each Block II equipment was a single, solid unit sealed in a special housing.

Development and production of the Apollo project at Collins Radio took nearly five years, and at its peak involved nearly 600 employees. Five other companies were key subcontractors to Collins for various units of the system, with Collins acting as system manager. Arthur Wulfsberg was program director, and Carl Henrici headed the subcontracting organization for Collins. Richard Pickering served as director of systems engineering.

Both individual and group quality performance awards

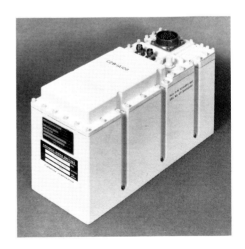

Block II Apollo communications equipment, such as this VHF/AM radio, was sealed in protective containers.

Assembly and inspection of Apollo equipment was performed in an area in Building 106 in Cedar Rapids. A chart on the wall showed the progress of each type of equipment.

were presented for achieving pre-established goals in the program. Employees earning quality performance awards were eligible for $100 savings bonds to be awarded every six months. "Silver Snoopy" awards were presented to 19 Collins employees, along with letters signed by astronauts expressing appreciation for their outstanding work. Receiving the awards were Jack Stewart, Gerald Hopkins, Lou Christiansen, John Zimmerman, Joe Stoos, Ruth Spurgeon, John Dutton, Boyd Palmer, Vern Jones, Ralph Hepker, Harold Oates, Richard Odell, Richard Rowland, Joe Maerschalk, Dale Thran, Richard Eidemiller, Robert Mitchell, Joseph Dahm and Rodney Peterson.

Communications/tracking system

In 1964, another significant Apollo contract went to Collins when it was selected by NASA to serve as the prime contractor for a worldwide network of communications/tracking earth stations.

The experience gained from Project Echo and the Pacific Missile Range led NASA to select Collins Radio to provide the 15 communications/tracking stations to keep the Apollo spacecraft in contact with mission control. The Unified S-Band System, as the network was known, was an improvement over earlier systems in that a single carrier frequency was used to convey all communications, as well as to determine the spacecraft's position. The $50 million contract was at that time the largest ever awarded to the Dallas Division.

Twelve stations employing 30-foot diameter antennas tracked the astronauts as they circled the earth. For the long distance trek to the moon and back, three large ground station 85-foot diameter antennas were used. In addition to this network of 15 ground stations, Collins supplied communica-

A full-scale mockup of the Apollo spacecraft was built by Collins and put on display for visitors.

tions and tracking equipment for use aboard ships and aircraft.

An additional $2.7 million Apollo contract was awarded to Collins in 1964. Under subcontract from RCA, Collins provided electronic equipment for the lunar excursion module.

The S-Band System of communications and tracking stations included shipboard installations, such as on the General H. H. Arnold *instrumentation ship.*

Left
Twelve stations were used to track and communicate with the Apollo spacecraft as it circled the earth. Each station, including the 30-foot diameter antenna and electronic equipment, was designed, constructed and installed by Collins and a team of subcontractors for NASA.

Pictures from the moon

On July 20, 1969, Apollo 11 landed on the moon. That night much of the world's population watched television signals, transmitted by Collins equipment, of Neil Armstrong and Edwin Aldrin, Jr. taking man's first steps on the moon, while Michael Collins (no relation to Arthur) orbited the moon in the command module.

"One of the things you think about is the feeling of accomplishment and personal participation. Everyone in Cedar Rapids certainly should be overjoyed," Arthur Collins said in a 1969 interview for the *Cedar Rapids Gazette.* Shifting any glory from himself, Collins said, "It was the people who did it." Although the system had been thoroughly checked, Collins said he too was surprised and pleased at the clarity of the transmission. "It was certainly very impressive. It represented a remarkable accomplishment in that it is a narrowband video channel, much less bandwidth than normally required for television."

It was later told that Collins had been invited to appear with Walter Cronkite during CBS's television coverage of the first landing. Collins declined, and let the glamor go elsewhere.

When the Apollo 11 astronauts returned, a hero's welcome awaited them around the world. The guest list for a state dinner for the astronauts, hosted by President Nixon, included Mr. and Mrs. Arthur A. Collins.

*Apollo 11 astronaut salutes the
American flag, July 1969.*

8

Growing markets

The year 1957 was a year of paradox for Collins Radio Company. It produced a greater volume of goods and services than at any time in its history, but net profit declined from the previous year.

It was a year in which Collins introduced many new products, especially in growing commercial fields, but research and development charges and tooling and start-up costs were high in relation to initial sales.

At the end of the 1957 fiscal year, the company's backlog of orders totaled $115 million — 25 percent higher than the year before. Much of the backlog consisted of research and development contracts.

Plans were made for constructing new facilities, financed by the sale of $8 million in debentures. A wholly-owned subsidiary, Texical, was formed to take title of real estate previously acquired by Collins in Cedar Rapids and Dallas, and to assume contracts for construction of new facilities. Under this arrangement, construction began at Dallas on a $1.5 million laboratory building to consolidate all engineering activities of the Texas Division. In Cedar Rapids, a $2.75 million project began for a new fabrication building (now known as Building 105) directly west of the engineering building. Two years earlier, Collins expanded its Cedar Rapids Division by leasing a 21,000 square foot factory in nearby Anamosa. Elmer Koehn was named manager for the Anamosa plant, which manufactured subassemblies.

Left
Collins telecommunications equipment was displayed at a 1960 Navy show in Washington, D.C. The company pioneered development and production of vehicular communications systems since World War II, and vehicular radios were used extensively in Vietnam.

Right
The 210,000-square-foot fabrication facility at Cedar Rapids (Building 105) was completed in 1959.

Though Collins' long-range product strategy included increasing transition from military to commercial uses, the yearly success of the company continued to rely heavily on government spending. In 1952, 90 percent of sales were to the U.S. Government. By 1957, the percentage of commercial sales had increased, but still stood at only 20 percent.

To broaden its base, Collins made an all-out effort to win new commercial contracts, particularly in the market for communication and navigation equipment for new jet airliners and expanding business aviation fleets. While it was successful in doing so, the initial costs in terms of engineering, tooling and start-up were large.

Despite attempts at Collins to become less dependent on military contracts, Department of Defense contract rescheduling in late 1957, coupled with the large facilities expansion program, hurt the company's financial picture. Big contracts, such as those for ARC-27 and GRC-27 UHF radios, were coming to a close.

As a result, operating results for the 1958 fiscal year were termed "unsatisfactory" in the annual report. The company showed a net loss of about $250,000 for the year, before a federal tax refund was figured in. Total employment at all locations dropped from 10,000 in 1957 to 7,750 the following year.

"Unsatisfactory though the year has been in terms of the financial results of its operations," Arthur Collins wrote in the company's 1958 annual report, "much has been accomplished in terms of operational reorganization of the parent company into five separate divisions, each of which has been made autonomous as to management. There has also been a modernization of facilities to improve efficiency, main-

The plant in Anamosa began operations in 1955.

Production areas in Building 106 featured "teleguides" in front of assembly operators to give detailed assembly instructions via an audio-visual presentation. 1961 photo.

tenance of working capital position and a substantial liquidation of inventories."

One year later, Collins reported its reorganization plans were paying off. Profits for 1959 were the highest in the company's 26-year history, topping $3.7 million. Employment rose from less than 8,000 to nearly 11,000. During the year an important phase of the company's long-range building program was completed with the addition of the new manufacturing building in Cedar Rapids and a new laboratory at Richardson. Plans were announced to build an additional 130,000-square-foot engineering and administrative building in Cedar Rapids (Building 106), and a 120,000-square-foot administrative and laboratory building at Newport Beach, California.

MOS chips were electrically tested by computer-generated test sequences at the Newport Beach facility. Operator is Erna Sanches. Lab technician is Chester Bishop.

Upper Right
The Newport Beach, California, facility was completed in 1961.

The Newport Beach facility, completed in 1961, housed the Information Science Center, where new designs in data communications equipment were undertaken by Collins Radio. West Coast operations moved from Burbank to Newport Beach in 1961, and the new facility became the headquarters for more than 1,000 employees.

Service division organized
In October, 1960, Collins Radio Company began a comprehensive review of field support requirements for the growing number of Collins equipments and systems in use around the globe. Company personnel experienced in support and maintenance activities and in marketing research techniques studied the problems of parts provisioning, field service engineering, factory repair and modifications, service parts supply, maintenance documentation and training in the electronics industry.

Out of this study plans were drawn to establish a service operation geared to the same standards of performance and quality as Collins equipment. The service division began

141

operations on Feb. 1, 1961. For the first time in company history, technical service and support responsibilities were consolidated under one management. The division's 625 employees were headed by R. F. Haglund, general manager. Regional field offices were located in New York, Miami, Burbank, and Seattle. International field service support was offered through offices in London, Toronto, Rio de Janeiro, Tokyo, Melbourne, and Frankfurt.

One key growth factor which led to establishing a separate service division was the wider use of integrated electronic systems produced by Collins. The increasing sophistication of such systems multiplied the requirements for competent technical support.

After a year of operation, the division held a contest to find a slogan to use throughout the electronics industry. Leon Glynn submitted the winning entry: "Collins Service: Around the Clock — Around the World."

Avionics

During the 1950s, aviation electronics (or "avionics" as the field was called) was the largest segment of Collins' business. By the end of the decade, the rate of growth had slowed somewhat, but avionics continued to be an important, growing and profitable business area for Collins.

Since its entry into avionics immediately following World War II and until the mid 1950s, Collins concentrated in the commercial aviation market on airliners and heavy business aircraft by providing equipment with the highest standards of performance and reliability. This emphasis paid off. Col-

Air Force One, the Presidential airplane, was placed in service in 1962 using communications equipment developed and manufactured by Collins. The aircraft is a VC-137, military version of the Boeing 707 airliner, modified to meet the special requirements of flying the President.

142

lins was recognized as a leader in both commercial and military aviation products. More than 80 percent of the new commercial jets — including the Boeing 707, Douglas DC-8, Convair 880, and the Lockheed Electra turboprop — carried Collins communication and navigation equipment. That figure excluded weather radar and autopilots — fields in which Collins was active in the 1950s but still a relative newcomer.

Foreseeing the need for lighter equipment to increase the payload of large aircraft as well as to meet the need in small aircraft for professional quality avionics, Collins in 1956 undertook a new research and development program. The goal was to produce flexible communications/navigation/flight control packages offering savings in size and weight, improve performance and reliability, and provide easier maintenance.

By using newer, lighter components it was possible for engineers to cut weight up to 60 percent. Using transistors where practical reduced size and power requirements. The use of modular design increased the flexibility of the equipment for varied applications, simplified maintenance and im-

This 1959 advertisement placed in several aviation magazines spoke of "The most complete line of high quality avionics equipment bearing one trademark."

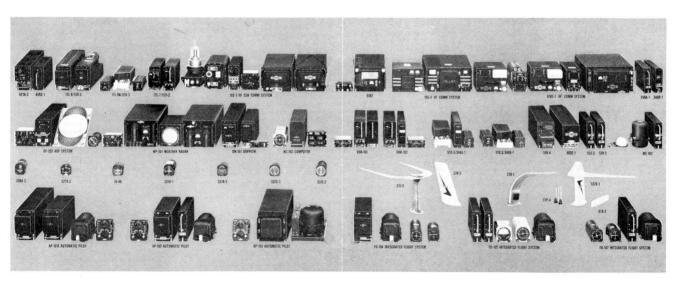

proved shock resistance and thermal design.

The first product designed for the expanding light aircraft market was the 17L-8 VHF transmitter. It represented quite a departure from other Collins airborne equipment, because it was designed for mounting behind the cockpit instrument panel. The radio offered commercial airline quality and reliability in a small size.

In 1958, Collins introduced its lightweight communication/navigation packages designed for all types of aircraft. Systems were configured for single-engine, light twin-engine, and medium and heavy twin engine aircraft. Included in this line was the 618F radio, the first VHF transceiver specifically designed for the general aviation market.

In 1960, the Doppler navigation system was added to the Collins line of avionics. By beaming microwave energy from an airplane toward the earth at several angles, the system, when used with a heading reference and a navigation computer, served as a completely self-contained navigation device.

Lightweight communication/navigation packages were exhibited at the Hotel Adolphus in Dallas in 1958. Pictured are Cal Glade and Craig Christie.

A navigation controversy

A requirement for a new type of airborne radio navigation aid was first generated by the airlines in 1951. The large air carriers were looking ahead to the inauguration of jet aircraft service by 1960. The decision on the first DME (distance measuring equipment), which used a pulse multiplex system and simple electronic ranging circuits, was delayed when the military came out in support of TACAN (tactical air navigation), another type of precise navigation system. TACAN, the military maintained, offered greater bearing accuracy flexibility, and could even be installed on ships. The two systems were incompatible from the standpoints of frequency allocation, economics and air traffic control.

The "TACANtroversy" raged until the President's Air Coordinating Committee established the common VORTAC system in 1956. TACAN facilities were installed at the VOR stations, with civil users relying on VOR and the military on TACAN for bearing guidance, and both relying on TACAN for distance information. A new high-performance DME system compatible with TACAN was developed in the early 1960s. By 1966, more than 800 new DME-equipped VOR stations were in operation in the United States, and distance service was also available from more than 200 military TACAN stations. Collins accommodated by building DME units for commercial aviation and TACAN units for the military.

The Collins 860E-2 distance measuring equipment featured solid state plug-in boards to make maintenance easier. For dual installation, a single indicator in the cockpit could show the distance to two different ground stations. 1966 photos.

Soon after the first flight of the Wright brothers flying machine on December 17, 1903, the aviation industry became acutely aware of the probability of midair collisions. In training and combat during World War I and World War II, both fledgling and seasoned aviators met untimely demises when their aircraft collided in that seemingly vast sea of blue sky.

With the tremendous proliferation of air commerce in the 1950s, it was only a matter of time before a catastrophic midair collision occurred in U.S. airspace. The collision of a Douglas DC-7 and Lockheed Constellation over the Grand Canyon in 1956 became the catalyst for investigation of possible collision avoidance systems.

The Air Transport Association began an earnest quest for a developmental program on collision avoidance equipment. From several pro-

posals submitted to the Air Transport Association, Collins was the first company selected to design and test a "noncooperative" collision avoidance system. Noncooperative meant that the equipment could detect all other aircraft, regardless of whether the others also had collision avoidance gear.

The basic requirement of a noncooperative system was a proximity indicator (PWI) that could determine the direction and range of other aircraft in the immediate vicinity. The effectiveness of such a system was very limited because the PWI required the flight crew to make visual contact with the intruder, executing evasive maneuvers at high closure rates. Additionally, an antenna of approximately 12 feet in diameter would have to be mounted on aircraft participating in the collision avoidance program.

Prototype systems were flown in

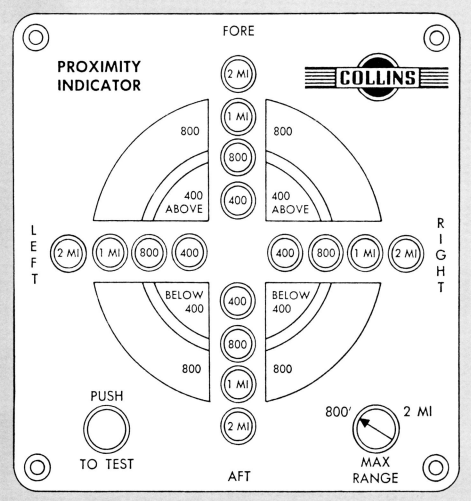

This drawing shows what Collins' proposed indicator would have looked like for a collision avoidance system in the 1950s. Quadrant and range information were to be shown by four rows of four lights. Upper and lower pairs of pie-shaped sectors would display hemispheric indication, including range.

company aircraft before it was conceded that a noncooperative system was not feasible with the electronic technology of the 1950s.

Competing airframe and avionics manufacturers tried unsuccessfully to gain FAA approval on varied collision avoidance systems. RCA submitted the SECANT system, McDonnell Douglas developed a time/frequency system and Honeywell produced the AVOIDS system.

In 1963, an industry-wide effort was undertaken to develop a "cooperative" collision avoidance system. To be considered a cooperative CAS, each aircraft had to be operating its equipment with the same time synchronization clock. Without accurate timing, collision avoidance computations could not be legitimate.

Having made very limited progress with collision avoidance systems during 1961 and 1962, the Federal Aviation Administration sought technical support from Collins. An effort was made to develop three cooperative CASs.

Through experimentation and practical application, it was apparent that the Time Frequency Range Altitude method of collision avoidance offered the most reliable means of detecting intruding aircraft.

Using data from Collins Radio, the Air Transport Association formed a CAS subcommittee in 1963. Comprised of leading manufacturers in the aircraft and avionics industry, the "Technical Working Group" determined that a noncooperative CAS was again not feasible with state-of-the-art avionics and engineering technology. Thousands of man-hours were spent in closed sessions during 1966 and 1967 to discuss the probable success of a cooperative Time Frequency Range Altitude collision avoidance system. By 1968, aircraft simulation programs were being designed for U.S. air carriers. A limited number of the (TFRA) CAS system simulators were delivered to the Piedmont Airline Pilot Training Center for evaluation.

Although the (TFRA) CAS system appeared to present a viable alternative for interrogating and avoiding intruder aircraft, this system required that all participating aircraft have compatible airborne collision avoidance systems. Considering that inflight aircraft testing was yielding poor results in the terminal area, and equipment costs would be exorbitantly high, it was not surprising the airlines were opposed to the Air Transport Association's recommendation that they purchase collision avoidance systems. Additionally, the general aviation version of the Time Frequency Range Altitude collision avoidance system was far too costly to manufacture to the complexity of the equipment.

Collins has not actively pursued the collision avoidance issue since 1969 because the Federal Aviation Administration and aviation industry at large have not made a firm decision about the direction which should be followed. Three distinct approaches, the Discreet Address Beacon System (DABS), Beacon Collision Avoidance System (BCAS) and Threat/Alert Collision Avoidance System (TCAS) have been reviewed, with TCAS favored by the FAA in 1983.

The DME airborne unit exchanged coded pulses with the ground station. The receiver in the aircraft measured the elapsed time between the transmitted pulses and the received pulses, and computed the aircraft's distance from the station. With DME, pilots could give more accurate position reports and estimated times of arrival. In turn, air traffic control could establish more accurate holding patterns and greater safety.

Introductions of Doppler navigation, transponders, and DME were closely followed in the fall of 1961 by what Paul Wulfsberg, Collins development department head, called "the biggest step in terms of technical advancement we have ever made between one generation of airborne equipment and another." Wulfsberg was referring to Collins' new Solid State Systems line. New developments in transistors, diodes and other solid state components allowed their use in the demanding environments of avionics. In many cases the new solid state design did away with all moving parts such as switches, gears, motors, and relays within the airborne units. Production of the solid state systems was designed to meet schedules of the second generation of jet airliners, such as the Boeing 727 in 1963.

A tour of Collins facilities was quickly arranged one day in 1962 when entertainer Danny Kaye flew his private airplane to Cedar Rapids for a visit. "My plane has much Collins equipment, and Collins makes the finest radio equipment in the world," Kaye told a reporter. Pictured from left are Kaye, Bob Winston, John Dayhoff, Glenn Bergmann and Clayton Lander.

Single sideband radio equipment for U.S. Army military vehicles was another growing market of the 1960s. To demonstrate the variety of Collins equipment for a visiting general, jeeps equipped with Collins radios were lined up in front of Building 121. Pictured from left: Arlo Meyer, Art Kemper, Paul Hoffman, Clay Kimsey, Leon Griswold, Joe Rosenberger, Bob Cribbs, Karl Stanley, Ed Andrade, Marv Gebr, Marion Albaugh, Roger Herreid, Ray Ruggiero, Evan Maloney, Clellan Wildes, Will Ogle, Hank Dmitruk, Bill Crawford, Jim Adelson, Wes Steele and Don Kent. 1961 photo.

The third dimension

Webster defines parallax as "the apparent displacement of an object observed due to a change or difference in the position of the observer." A common example of this, as it pertains to instrument interpretation, is the automobile speedometer which indicates a different speed to the passenger in the right front seat than to the driver who is seated directly in front of the instrument.

In instruments where exact readings are critical, parallax is reduced to an absolute minimum by positioning the pointer as closely as possible to the instrument face. This is simple enough, but what if more than one pointer is required and each requires full freedom of movement? What could be done if the background of the instrument must move and six, eight or even ten indicators must also move and retain their proper relationship regardless of the angle from which the instrument is viewed?

This was the problem handed to Collins engineers in 1961. The instrument specifically under consideration was a new flight director indicator which would enable jet airliners to operate effectively under the same landing minimums as conventionally-powered aircraft.

It was a real challenge, and Collins engineers, principally Harry Passman and Horst Schweighofer, decided on a radical new approach. They changed the way the information was displayed by consolidating pitch and roll commands into a V-shaped bar, and changing the aircraft symbol to a large

The Collins V-bar flight director indicator consists of a small orange-colored, delta-winged airplane symbol appropriately mounted in front of a two-color movable horizon background. This indicates the aircraft's pitch and roll attitude in a conventional relationship. Pitch and roll commands are provided by a set of yellow-colored V-shaped bars that create the illusion of a track in the sky which the pilot follows with the miniature aircraft.

In an approach to a runway with the instrument, if the airplane needs to fly up and to the right to intercept the glideslope and localizer signals from the ground, the V-bars will be positioned above the airplane and tilted to the right.

Pilot reactions to commands presented this way are instinctive and positive. Because both pitch and roll commands are presented on one indicator, the pilot makes simultaneous corrections of pitch and bank rather than making them separately as is often the case when these commands are presented on separate needles.

Commands presented on the V-bars can be derived from a variety of sources. In the pitch axis, for example, the V-bars may be used to command a selected climbout angle, maintain a selected altitude or follow the glideslope on an instrument approach. In the roll axis, the V-bars can be used to command bank angles required to reach and maintain a magnetic heading or follow a VOR or localizer course.

In addition to steering commands, the pilot of an aircraft making an instrument approach wants to see his actual aircraft position relative to the localizer and glidesloper to make sure the steering computer is working properly. In the Collins 3-D indicator, the aircraft position relative to the glideslope is shown by a pointer and scale on the left side of the instrument. Displacement from the localizer centerline is shown by the lateral movement of a miniature runway symbol at the bottom of the instrument.

United States Patent Office

Des. 194,191
Patented Dec. 4, 1962

194,191
FLIGHT DIRECTOR AIRCRAFT INSTRUMENT
Horst M. Schweighofer, 2849 14th Ave. SE., and Harry M. Passman, 2848 Seely Ave. SE., both of Cedar Rapids, Iowa

Filed June 5, 1961, Ser. No. 65,462

Term of patent 14 years

(Cl. D52—6)

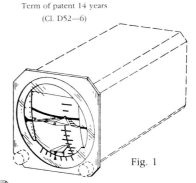

Fig. 1

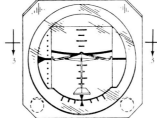

Fig. 2

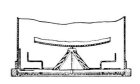

Fig. 3

FIGURE 1 is a front perspective view of a flight director aircraft instrument showing our new design;
FIGURE 2 is a front elevational view thereof; and
FIGURE 3 is a reduced section taken on line 3—3 of FIGURE 2.
The essential features of the design reside in the full line portions.
We claim:
The ornamental design for a flight director aircraft instrument, as shown and described.

References Cited in the file of this patent
UNITED STATES PATENTS
2,655,046   Seifried --------------Oct. 13, 1953
2,912,766   Hurlburt -----------Nov. 17, 1959

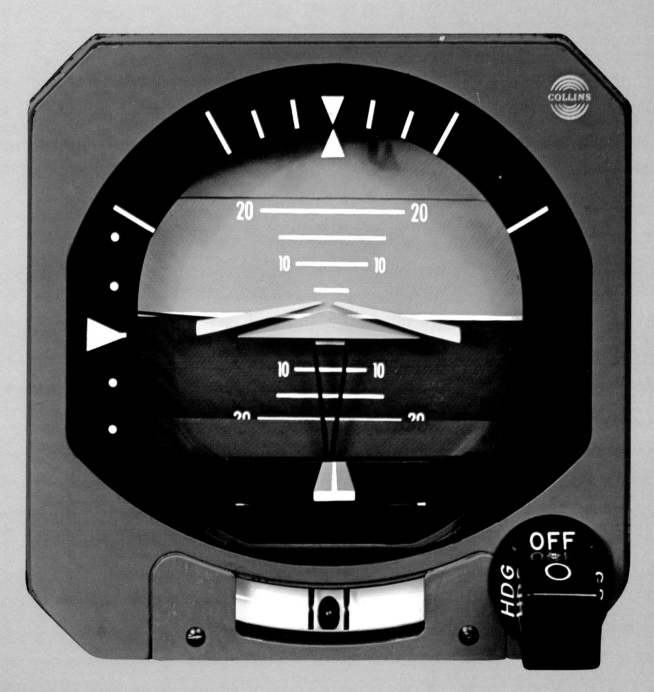

*The "V-bar" indicator gave
pilots a new way to view
flight information.*

delta shape. The idea was simple and elegant. It was the natural way to display flight information, as pilots and other flight instrument manufacturers soon discovered.

The first FD-108s incorporating the three-dimensional V-bar steering were delivered to Trans World Airlines in 1963 for new Boeing 727 jetliners. Braniff Airways installed V-bar indicators in new BAC-111s and retrofitted them in Boeing 707s and 720s. Eventually the V-bar became an industry standard, and most avionics manufacturers now offer a choice of V-bar or cross-pointer steering on their flight director instruments.

Down the path to zero-zero

Since its entry into avionics, Collins was a major contributor to battle against aviation's chief enemy — bad weather.

In 1964, the Federal Aviation Administration estimated weather delays, diversions, and cancellations cost the airlines more than $67 million that year. The industry wanted a solution to the costly problem. Working with the airlines, the pilots, and the avionics manufacturers, the FAA established a schedule for achieving "zero-zero" landings (landings accomplished with a zero altitude cloud ceiling and zero visibility).

The first step, called Category I, designated that airplanes were legally allowed to land with a minimum of a 200-foot ceiling over the airport and one-half-mile of visibility at the runway threshold. These were the legal minimums at the time the categories were established.

Chart depicts step-by-step categories involved in achieving all-weather landing capability.

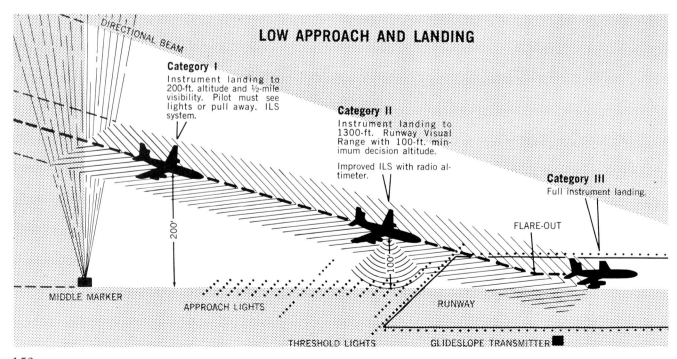

LOW APPROACH AND LANDING

DIRECTIONAL BEAM

Category I
Instrument landing to 200-ft. altitude and ½-mile visibility. Pilot must see lights or pull away. ILS system.

Category II
Instrument landing to 1300-ft. Runway Visual Range with 100-ft. minimum decision altitude.

Improved ILS with radio altimeter.

Category III
Full instrument landing.

FLARE-OUT

200'

100'

MIDDLE MARKER

APPROACH LIGHTS

RUNWAY

THRESHOLD LIGHTS

GLIDESLOPE TRANSMITTER

Category II, the next step, meant that certified airplanes could land with a 100-foot ceiling and one-quarter-mile runway visibility. Collins developed the avionics which enabled the first certified Category II landing, achieved on January 12, 1966, by a Jet Commander business airplane.

Next came Category IIIA, which brought the minimum runway visibility requirement down to 700 feet. Again, Collins was the first avionics manufacturer to have its equipment certified. The effort began in 1968 when a team of Collins Radio and Lear Siegler was selected by Lockheed Aircraft to develop the flight control system for its new L-1011 TriStar jetliner. The pairing of Collins with Lear Seigler of Santa Monica, California, combined Lear Seigler's experience in automatic landing flareout techniques with Collins' record for airline service and support, derived from other avionics business with the carriers.

The contract was one of the largest ever awarded in commercial avionics history, covering 350 aircraft and amounting to more than $40 million.

On April 27, 1971, the Collins FCS-110 automatic flight control system was the first equipment of its kind to be certified by the FAA for Category IIIA landings.

"It was phenomenal for such a sophisticated system to

perform so perfectly on the first try," said E. L. Joiner, the TriStar's chief flight test engineer for Lockheed. Joiner said the pilot just pushed a button "and the plane did the rest."

An example of the efficiency of the automatic system was demonstrated in a subsequent landing at Palmdale, California, site of Lockheed's test facility. A conventional commercial jet airliner making a manual approach under gusty crosswind conditions was rolling and pitching in the turbulence, with the pilot working hard to maintain the desired flight path. The L-1011 following this airliner was using its new autopilot to make an automatic landing. To ground observers, the L-1011 appeared to be "riding on rails" compared to the other airliner.

In 1970, a new kind of navigation system that made its debut with the new generation of wide-body airliners had far-reaching effects on the way airlines went about their business.

Above
Pilot and copilot make a "hands off" automatic landing of a Lockheed L-1011 jetliner.

Lower
An L-1011 makes an automatic landing.

The first system of this new class to go into regular service was called the Collins AINS-70 Area-Inertial Navigation System. Employing a digital computer in its most expanded application in civil air transportation, the AINS-70 automated both short- and long-range navigation, with automatic flight plan execution. It was the first commercial airborne application of the Collins C-System — a digital computer-based system integrating communication, computation and control. Two cathode ray tube (CRT) display units presented each pilot with selected navigation information, and each had a keyboard for the pilot to enter instructions, call for a display of flight data, insert information or modify flight plans. The advanced system was installed aboard the McDonnell Douglas DC-10.

The AINS-70 automated both short- and long-range navigation for DC-10 jetliners, beginning in the early 1970s. The flight crew could program navigation information on the keyboards and see information displayed on the CRT screens.

9
Computer systems

At the beginning of the 1960s, Collins policy-makers felt that an extraordinary increase in industrial data communications was about to take place. Computers had reached the point of development where communication of their data had become a major problem. A single computer had a communications requirement equivalent to the work capacity of many human beings. Collins felt the demand was pressing for new communications systems, and particularly efficient use of the present ones.

Computer design was not new territory for the company. Collins experience in computer systems dated back to research in small airborne units for flight control, and high capacity data transmission in the late 1940s.

Practical theories and mathematical analyses of data transmission were formally presented in a 1949 paper, "Radiotelegraphy," by Walter Wirkler, and in a 1951 paper, "Communications Systems Analyses," by M. L. Doelz.

The first results of the research in high-speed data transmission were Predicted Wave Signaling systems, which were based upon improved frequency stability, integration and synchronization techniques. Their capacity to handle information in bits per second was more than twice as efficient as any other form of data signaling developed by that time.

One of the early tests involved a Cedar Rapids-to-Dallas radio circuit in 1952 and 1953. The predicted wave equipment was tested by Collins and Bell Telephone Laboratories in 1954, resulting in selection of predicted wave signaling for the DEW Line.

Data transmission was refined and in 1957, the name was changed to Kineplex®. With its related terminal equipment for handling punch cards, paper, magnetic tape or other information sources, the system constituted Collins' entry into the data communications field. Kineplex, which was fully-transistorized, was designed to operate on available communications channels, whether they were telephone lines, microwave, single sideband, or scatter radio transmission.

By adding or replacing modules of the Collins C-8500 computer series, the user could build and expand the system to meet his requirements.

157

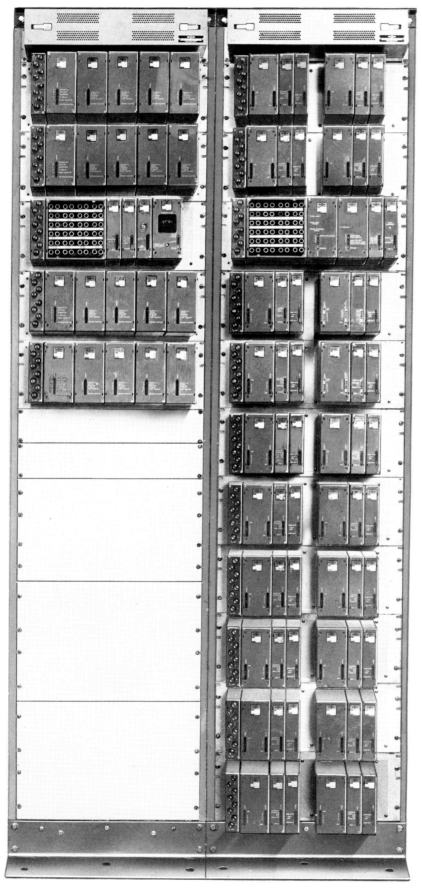

The Collins TE-202 modem, which was about the size of a refrigerator, was part of the Kineplex system. 1959 photo.

In the late 1950s, the principal customer was the military, which used Kineplex data links to couple processing centers handling missile data, for missile range installations, for tactical deployment, and for world-wide logistics. In one military system, known as Naval Tactical Data System (NTDS), functions such as detecting and tracking enemy and friendly forces were worked out in computers to coordinate an entire naval task force. NTDS gave the task force commander a complete, overall tactical picture of the task force situation.

From the early days of the company's research efforts in the field of synchronous communications, Collins sold electronic devices, called modems, which allowed computers to talk with each other over telephone lines and reliable radio circuits. The first Collins modem was introduced in 1955. The TE-202 was about the size of a refrigerator and weighed 700 pounds. Collins became the world's largest independent producer of data modems at 2,400, 3,600 and 4,800 bits per second. The modems were used in surface and airborne radios, and wireline data systems.

By 1961, Collins Radio had established profitable operations in military and commercial electronics, and its telecommunications business was growing rapidly.

The logical choice for a new segment of business, as Arthur Collins saw it, was digital computers which could handle both data processing and telecommunication message switching, among other tasks. The major competitor was IBM, which dominated wide portions of the computer market at the time. Other companies had spent large sums of money in apparent efforts to parallel the position of IBM, but Collins decided on a different approach.

Collins had been successful in challenging established competition by making an energetic effort toward selected markets. A "rifle rather than a shotgun approach" was how the 1963 annual report described Collins' approach to the computer market. But Arthur Collins felt it could not be a limited effort. If his company failed to develop a complete and superior system, it would be inconsistent with company policy.

Research began for computers that would be true general purpose-machines with enough versatility to be equally at home with communication processes (such as teletype message switching, priority routing, and data transmission and conversion) as well as with conventional data processing operations. Collins engineers reasoned that communications could borrow much from computer technology, since storing, selecting and processing data were fundamental to both. They recognized that by properly programming a computer, various basic communications processes could be regulated with greater efficiency and accuracy, and with smaller-sized equipment.

Before development work got too far along, Collins engineers looked into existing computers to determine whether they could be adapted or modified for communications work. They found most were inefficient for communications, largely because they could handle a given number of specific problems, but lacked the "general purpose" flexibility a communications-oriented computer needed.

The Collins approach to the problem was to create a flexible computer. A magnetic core memory, which could operate 15 times faster than the main memory, took the place of "fixed-wire" logic.

A second major design feature was to improve both internal and external communication capability. This was done by using a high-speed transfer link or common data bus. In effect, the transfer link, coupled with appropriate data transmission terminals, provided complete freedom of data transfer between all peripheral equipment.

To demonstrate what high speed data transmission could do, Collins established a data processing center in Cedar Rapids in the spring of 1961. The $1 million, two-story structure (Building 121), located next to the engineering building, became the nerve center of the company. Facilities at Texas, Toronto and the new Information Science Center at Newport Beach *(See Chapter 8)* were linked via Kineplex with Collins Data Central. Links were also added to computers operating in Kansas City, Washington and New York.

In addition to serving as a working demonstration of Kineplex, the data processing center was a pioneering effort toward improving basic management techniques through rapid and precise transmission and processing of all types of business data. Inventory, shipping, receiving, production and payroll records and other information necessary for daily operations were processed at the center for the various locations on the system. The centralized data processing concept was expanded to include voice, teletype and facsimile service. As it took shape, it became a communication *and* data processing system, with equal emphasis on both elements.

After the "bugs" were worked out with the system installed at Collins, a commercial version was developed. Development of the C-8400 System started in May, 1961, and just 13 months later the first pilot system was operating.

One of the first installations of the system was made for Aeronautical Radio, Inc., (ARINC) for use as an airline

The Collins Data Central building (Building 121) in Cedar Rapids was constructed to showcase the company's developments in computer systems and provide a test facility for C-System technology.

Because of the complexity of the C-8400 system, assembly was no easy task, as evidenced by the web of wires which had to be correctly attached.

teletype message processing and switching center at Elk Grove Village, Illinois. The facility interconnected circuits for airline offices throughout the United States and overseas. An installation ordered by the New York Central Railroad represented the first railroad application of such equipment for automatic assembly and distribution of messages and data information. Collins Data Central in Cedar Rapids acted as a classification and distribution point for all the messages transmitted throughout the systems.

An evaluation of the computer systems two years later showed costs related to initial customer orders were running higher than the revenue generated.

"It is anticipated that continuing commitments for servicing these customers will adversely affect 1965 earnings to a lesser extent, and that orders undertaken subsequently will be profitable," Arthur Collins wrote for the 1964 annual report.

In 1966, Collins took another technological step by introducing the C-8500 computer system, which combined multispeed communication with business and scientific data computation for control of on-line, real-time operations. Using microminiature integrated circuit components, the new computer group was designed in modular packages similar to the black boxes manufactured for commercial airliners. This design allowed the customer to customize his system by simply adding or replacing modules.

Providing a system-oriented configuration and a simplified maintenance program through unit replacement, the C-8500 computer used modules of the same size used by the air transport industry for avionics racking.

Opposite Page
The magnetic core memory of the C-8400 system took the place of "fixed-wire" logic. Because command sequences were stored magnetically in this memory, the Collins computer could be "rewired" for a new application by reading in a new logic program.

Computer systems

The C-8500, part of the "C-System," made available to users the first completely integrated communication, computation and control system having virtually unlimited expansion capability.

Arthur Collins, believing the market potential for C-System applications was huge, personally supervised much of the computer system's development and plans for marketing.

"This continuing development of communication, computation and control systems is of particular significance for long-range expansion of market potential," he stated in the 1968 annual report.

With the C-System, it was no longer necessary to isolate accounting, engineering, manufacturing, communications, personnel and general management functions. The C-System had the ability to accommodate all these functions.

In 1966, Collins undertook an extensive program to construct facilities for process production which resulted in addition of 1.4 million square feet, bringing the total facility area to 4.1 million square feet. Also, extensive modifications were made in existing plant space for advanced technical operations. These expansions occurred in Cedar Rapids, Dallas, Newport Beach and Toronto, as well as in Frankfurt, West Germany, and Melbourne, Australia.

Collins Data Central in Cedar Rapids after installation of C-8500 equipment.

164

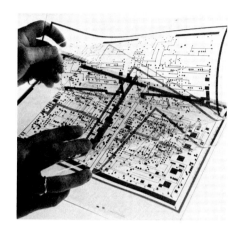

Each photoplate copy of a multi-layer circuit board layer shows the patterns of the various circuits.

C-System techniques were applied to teleproduction — using the computer to produce manufactured products. Blank multilayer circuit boards were fed by a special conveyor into machines that etched away unwanted copper. Internal circuit layer patterns were protected by a coating of photoresist during etching, while external layer patterns were protected by a tin overplate.

The 240,000-square-foot solid state device plant at Newport Beach, placed in operation in 1969, was the final unit of this construction project.

Collins called this new form of computer-controlled operation "teleproduction," a term which it applied to using sophisticated computers not only in management and design, but also in the output of products or physical work.

Collins provided teleproduction services, the highly automated design, fabrication, and testing facilities for multilayer circuit boards, hybrid microcircuits, and metal oxide semiconductor (MOS) arrays for its own engineering force and outside customers. By the late 1960s, Collins was a major supplier of hybrid microcircuits.

Although multilayer circuit boards had been used for several years, the advancements of MOS/LSI (large scale integration) technology increased the need for dense multilayer interconnects. Collins' use of computer-oriented layout and numerically-controlled fabricating machines provided the capability to manufacture boards of two to 14 layers in as little as 14 days.

The MOS/LSI array held between the fingertips replaced the hybrid thin film (shown under array) on this transmit board of a Collins data set.

In September, 1968, company officials announced the beginning of a vigorous program to sell its C-System to industry and government. Collins believed that it could compete in the computer market and capture a sizeable portion with its system. The company cited several reasons, including easier maintenance, greater flexibility, higher efficiency, and the capability for computer control of manufacturing.

The announcement of entry into the commercial computer industry followed reports of record earnings and sales for the 1968 fiscal year. Collins noted that the sale of computer services would have minimal effect on fiscal 1969 operating results, because it usually took more than a year to bid for, produce and deliver the equipment.

"Collins is in fact so advanced in computer technology," said the April 24, 1969, issue of the *New York Times,* "that it may be standing on the threshold of a new era.

"Collins Radio's radical approach to computer technology contrasts dramatically to the normal approach. The normal approach, dictated by the inability of present computers to handle information from a variety of points of views, is to look at a single problem at a time — as though boxed apart from everything else. Thus, a single computer user might have to rent time on one computer suited to handling engineering problems, a second one capable of handling automated manufacturing machines, a third to do the billing, a fourth to handle payroll, etc.

166

"But Collins has designed a single system to eliminate much duplication and results in one memory bank into which segments of a single computer can 'dip and fuel' at will."

Collins hoped that in addition to developing a market for computer services, the use of these services would lead directly to computer system installations for customers as they developed their own integrated management information, design and production control systems.

To fully develop the market potential, it was necessary for many current computer users to completely "scrap" what they were using and invest in the Collins equipment. Many in the industry doubted that this would happen, but Arthur Collins' previous record of successes in anticipating the needs of the electronics marketplace convinced him, and others, he was right.

But in this instance, time ran out before the market and the product got together.

The effort to sell the C-System included an elaborate exhibit booth complete with operating computer systems for demonstrations to convention visitors.

Collins Sales, Earnings Down; Improvement Seen

d, Collins pected, the company said. A delay in government procurement programs dealt a blow to the results.

Backlog of orders at the end of the year was $304 million, up from $285 million a year earlier, the company said.

Collins noted its participation as a communications contractor for the successful Apollo moon mission in 1969 was...

That was the problem when Electronic Data tried taking over Collins with an offer that was theoretically worth 30% more than Collins' recent market price? Simply this: Some big Collins stockholders felt that their $166 million might be worth more in real money than EDS $597 million. They have a point: For the last nine months, Collins' earnings were $8.3 million vs. $2 million for EDS.

What made EDS worth 300 times earnings vs. 12 times for Collins? One reason: 91% of EDS stock is held by Perot and his board; the high price of the stock is based on a small float and on very little trading. Collins' price was established in a real auction market.

H. Ross Perot

that both sales and earnings for the year ended Aug. 1 were down sharply.

Sales for the year totaled $400,223,000, down from $447,025,000 a year earlier. Net income totaled $8,922,000, down from...

Collins Radio Hits Electronic Data's Take-Over Offer

Collins Board Indicates It Is Weighing Other Proposals From a Number of Firms

Opposition to Plan Detailed

By NORMAN PEARLSTINE
Staff Reporter of THE WALL STREET JOURNAL

DALLAS—Collins Radio Co. directors rejected a take-over bid by Electronic Data Systems Corp. and indicated they are weighing alternative proposals from a number of other firms in Collins.

McDonnell Douglas Corp. and University Computing Co. are among McDonnell Douglas Corp. and University Computing Co. are among the companies that have expressed an interest in Collins.

Arthur A. Collins, chairman, president and founder of the diversified electronic communications company, mentioned the proposals in a letter to stockholders detailing the company's opposition to a tender offer for Collins common shares by Electronic Data, a small Dallas concern engaged in the design, installation and operation of computer systems.

Mr. Collins said the company has been evaluating a number of transactions "which, if consummated, might have an important effect on the current situation and the future of Collins."

A Collins official added that "more than 10 companies have approached Collins indicating a willingness to assist in solving problems raised by Electronic Data's proposed exchange offer." He would neither confirm nor deny that...

The Cedar Rapids Gazette

EASTERN IOWA'S LEADING DAILY
10 CENTS

CEDAR RAPIDS, IOWA, THURSDAY, MAY 8, 1969   ASSOCIATED PRESS, UPI, NEW YORK TIMES

Story of the Attempt to Take Over Collins Radio Co.

(This article is published in The Gazette by special permission of the Wall Street Journal in which it appeared May 8, 1969.)

Using the simple device of a common stock tender offer, Mr. Perot planned to swap his stock — selling at some 300 times earnings — for the depressed shares of financially troubled Collins.

Withdrew

But last week Mr. Perot wore a long face. He withdrew his tender offer as suddenly as he had made it, explaining that bank loan agreements of the Collins contained a default clause that might jeopardize the proposed take-over.

The terse withdrawal statement hid more that it reveal... so it seems to a close

observer of the internal maneuvers of both companies during the five-week struggle. The events of those weeks are a textbook study of how an apparently vulnerable company fended off an unwanted suitor.

At the center of this drama was Arthur A. Collins, 60-year-old chairman and president of Collins Radio. He founded the firm in the basement of his parents' Cedar Rapids, Iowa, home 45 years ago.

An intense scientist, he personally has developed many of the company's electronic patents. "His laboratory is his life," observes one company engineer, who adds that Mr. Collins spent long hours on his pet lab projects even during the thick of the battle with Electronic Data.

Waiting Game

But Mr. Collins' activities were deceptive. He played a careful waiting game and,

with unyielding pride, refused to even see Mr. Perot after the tender offer was made.

In the struggle between these two strong personalities, big institutional investors finally threw in their chips and scornfully that "the chairman's place is in the board room looking out for stockholders, not in the laboratory."

To him, Arthur Collins is one of the great living geniuses of electronic communications" but a less - than adequate executive. "His job is to conduct the symphony, with what one financial analyst calls "the most incredible ineptitude for telling its story to Wall Street," has soured many investors on Collins Radio.

Some charged that Mr. Collins had buried himself in research and was oblivious to stockholder interests. The pessimism was reflected in a 50 percent slide in the market

value of Collins stock in the past 15 months.

Running a Business

To Mr. Perot, the moment was right for Electronic Data to strike. Munching a cold cheeseburger in his office, he said scornfully that "the chairman's place is in the board room looking out for stockholders, not in the laboratory."

To him, Arthur Collins is one of the great living geniuses of electronic communications" but a less - than adequate executive. "His job is to conduct the symphony, all he does is play the drums, leaving no one in charge."

Mr. Perot clearly sees himself as a man who can conduct a business. He formed Electronic Data in 1962 after working five years for International Business Machines chairman, president

stockholder, with 81 percent of the outstanding shares.

When he went public in September 1968, buyers snapped up $50,000 shares at $16.50 a share — or 118 times fiscal 1968 earnings. The stock soared to $40 by January this year, helped by the fact that Electronic Data earnings last year were 85 times the level three years earlier.

Approached Collins

With his stock at this lofty level, Mr. Perot decided to approach Arthur Collins in January with merger plans. Mr. Perot noted that the market value of his company was close to half a billion dollars — far more than the $150 million value of Collins stock, then selling at $50 a share. Collins' shares were being traded at less than 12

from merger when it became clear Mr. Perot would assume control of any combined company.

On Saturday, March 22 Electronic Data informed Collins it was planning a tender offer to Collins stockholders. Two days later it made public the offer to exchange Electronic Data common stock with a market value of $65 for each Collins share up to a total of 82 percent of Collins stock — with a maximum of 1.5 Electronic Data shares to be swapped for each Collins share.

Agitated

Mr. Collins was livid. For the next five weeks his cigaret consumption was to climb to more than three packs a day from the usual two. But his top aides were even more agitated.

one or face being taken over," David H. Foster, vice-president and director told a reporter at Collins headquarters. W. W. Roodhouse, the company's executive vice-president, who had come into the only nod assent in silence.

But Mr. Col hasty action. "W out a lot of rough the last 15 somehow we'll out, too," he sa reaction was that was impossible.

But after thre steady argument lawyers and oth him the threat wa

Perot Ju

Meanwhile, Me his associates Me the first week tender announce

Collins Sales, Earnings Down; Improvement Seen

Collins Radio Co. Tuesday announced earnings for the three months ended Nov. 1, 1968, of $2.1 million, or 69 cents per share based on 2,967,427 shares outstanding.

Earnings for the prior fiscal year were $2.5 million, or 81 cents per share based on 2,832,711 average shares. Sales in the current fiscal quarter were $95 million, compared with $112 million a year ago.

E. A. Williams, vice-president, control and finance, speaking at Collins' stockholders' meeting in Cedar Rapids Tuesday, said the lower sales and earnings in the first quarter of fiscal 1969 were primarily attributable to a

reduction in the company's booking level of government contracts during the last several months.

He noted that the first quarter results represent an anticipated low for the fiscal year to be followed by progressively improving quarters.

Backlog at Nov. 1, 1968, was $318 million compared to $465 million on Nov. 3, 1967, and $339 million on Aug. 2, 1968.

"While this is a difficult point at which to make projections," Williams said, "especially in relation to the timing of events which will determine the company, we believe the year's total sales will approximate $410 to $420 million, with earnings in the range of $3.50 to $3.80 per share."

Collins' board of directors also declared a quarterly cash dividend of 20 cents per share of common stock payable Jan. 13, 1969, to stockholders of record on Dec. 22, 1968. All of the

WALL STREET JO

© 1969 Dow Jones & Company, Inc. All Rights Reserved.

MONDAY, APRIL 21, 1969

Collins Radio, Honeywell Talks Collapse, Leaving Collins to Fend Smaller Firm's Bid

bid of about $70 a share was strong enough to defeat Electronic Data's proposed offer, whether Honeywell was willing to increase its offer, initially if it became necessary.

OFFICIAL BID FOR COLLINS

Leased Wire From Dow Jones

DALLAS, TEX. — Electronic Data Systems Corp. of Dallas, Wednesday filed with the Securities and Exchange Commission its proposed tender offer to shareholders of Collins Radio Co. of Dallas and Cedar Rapids, Ia.

The company had said Monday that it intended to make a bid for Collins' stock.

Electronic Data, which noted that it already holds 75,000 Collins Radio common shares, said it seeks at least 1,438,363 more to give it at least 51 percent of Collins' 2,967,427 outstanding shares.

Under terms of the Electronic Data offer, the company will exchange a maxi-

THE BUSINESS TIDE

Collins Board Rejects Bid, Hints Other Offers

Leased Wire to The Register

Directors of Collins Radio Co. of Cedar Rapids, Ia., and Dallas, Tex., rejected a takeover bid by Electronic Data Systems Corp., Dallas, and indicated they are weighing alternative proposals from several other companies.

In a letter to stockholders Monday, Arthur A. Collins, chairman, president and founder of the diversified electronic communications company, said the Electronic Data proposal was "hostile to the interests of the company and its shareholders," and that the Collins board "has unanimously decided to oppose vigorously," the offer.

Willing to Assist

The chairman noted that management has been evaluating a number of transactions "which, if consummated, might have an important effect on the current situation and the future of Collins."

A Collins official added that "more than 10 companies have approached Collins indicating a willingness to assist in solving problems raised by Electronic Data's proposed exchange offer." The official declined to elaborate.

Electronic Data, a small concern engaged in design, installation and operation of computer systems, announced last week that it seeks at least 1,438,363 Collins common shares, which with the 75,000 shares it already holds, would give it at least 51 per cent of

Honeywell Inc. and Collins Talk Merger

Cedar Rapids News—

Merger discussions have been started by officials of Collins Radio Co. and Honeywell Inc., Minneapolis, officials of both companies announced T...

In a brief statement, Chairman James H. B... Honeywell and Arthur... Collins, chairman and pres... Collins Radio, the co... said terms of the p... transaction have not y... arrived at.

They said furthe... nouncements will be m... negotiations continue.

Automation Compa

Tuesday's annou... came on the heels of a... take-over of Collins b... tronic Data Systems of I... much smaller compan... EDS much tender off... nounced two weeks ago,... resisted by Collins mana...

Honeywell, which ha... of more than two and

times those of Collins, describes itself as an

rst Quarter ported by Collins

ported in acting period in the year, both in sales and earnings.

"While this particularly exacting period in the nation's economy is a difficult time to make projections, our best judgment presently is that the year's total sales will be slightly below that of 1970 and earnings will see a fair improvement. In making this projection, we have anticipated a low sales volume/rate in the first quarter and its effect...

COLLINS NET DOWN 29%

Leased Wire From Dow Jones

DALLAS, TEX. — Collins Radio Co., Tuesday coupled announcements of a 29.3 per cent drop in nine-months earnings and a forecast of a "20 to 30 per cent" increase in earnings for the fiscal year ended July 31,...

THE BUSINESS TIDE

Collins Radio's Earnings, Sales Off for Quarter

Leased Wire to The Register

Collins Radio Co., large Cedar Rapids, Ia., and Dallas, Tex., manufacturer of electronic equipment suffered a 10.5 per cent decline in earnings for the quarter ended Nov. 1, the first period of fiscal 1969, as sales slipped

with a 80-cent dividend rate is 1.2 per cent.

Banks Were Leery

(Continued from Page 1)

saw no major bars to total success. And they talked of combining their own knowledge of computers with Collins' broad communications and electronics experience to create a rival to IBM by 1980.

Their optimism was fueled by the quick jump in Collins' stock to more than $60 a share following announcement of the tender offer. More than 272,000 Collins shares were traded in the five days following the announcement, suggesting that institutional investors were buying large quantities of Collins stock because they thought the Electronic Data offer would succeed.

Two weeks after the announcement, Mr. Perot knew that 10 institutional investors held more than one million Collins shares, or one-third of Collins, and that they would hold the key to victory or defeat.

Two days after the offer was made, Mr. Perot was predicting privately that he would have commitments from major holders of more than 500,000

ARTHUR COLLINS

reservations to any merger with Collins, sources say. Mr. Perot apparently knew about the opposition treasury department's opposition before Collins officials did.

Mr. Perot denies he ever spoke with Attorney General John Mitchell about Control Data. But he is a long-time friend of the attorney general, worked with him during the Nixon campaign and has used President Nixon's former law firm for personal matters.

In the first week after the announcement of the tender offer, Mr. Perot's only failure was his inability to get Arthur Collins to meet him to discuss a "friendly deal." The Electronic Data's executive knew his chances would improve if Mr. Collins and other board members accepted the tender offer.

Grounds for Optimism

"The rise in the cost of money eliminates potential borrowers [who might make a competing offer]," he said. "Action by the treasury department knocks out the conglomerates. Congressman Mills' criticism of the use of debentures to finance take-overs will knock out others. And the

to other Collins like this: Mr. have to participate offer, the prospect would have th... other Collins... Rather, after... was completed... would merge... through a tax... tion, allowing... change his shar...

Some securit... question whether... arrangement... carried out... disclosure in... covering the... shares to be... change.

There were... Mr. Collins th... cussed at his... porter one eve... take-over stra... [the present... Collins chroni... Data. It would... Collins to bu... division or m... whole company... "I would ha... company to..."

Went
The prosp... ing that Mr... the end of th... a vacation... the Bahama... tronic Data... keep tab on... mote the El... New York S... Collins bro... ticity the se...

to the interests holders" and to mously decide offer.

With other con ers that Collins tender offer wo find another m 20% of Collins... If another prop Electronic D and couldn't b "line" announce

Electronic seeks at least which, with... would give it shares outstand

Under term tronic Data w having a majo share tendered tronic Data s lins share. Ele 2,430,000 Coll the outstandin 3,645,000 sha...

New York Stock Excha Thursday, on $9.875 for the over the count asked on Fri banned credit...

In opposing lins said that earnings and tions supplie... statement, the... in excess o... 91% of Elec million share officers and o owned by offi...

The letter... of trading" h... suffer...

For exa... a share... ants if 20... range on... should or... while tryin... e, Collins ared on... r future....

to gulp a big one

nic Data Systems proposes Co. Collins opposes the deal, well and other companies

The Cedar Rapids Gazette

Editorial Page

Sunday, May 11, 1969

Collins Showed Mettle

IF Wall Street Journal reporter Norman Pearlstine's account of the recent abortive effort to take over the Collins Radio Company is reasonably accurate—and we have no reason to doubt it—the people of

pleasant to watch from the sidelines an uncommonly audacious attempt to restructure an industry so important to the Cedar Rapids economy against the re-

Battle for Survival

A few years ago, Arthur Collins of Collins Radio bet heavily on a new computer. Right now, he appears to be losing that bet.

The C-System has caused much of Collins' trouble. Its research and development costs, though scattered over several product lines and therefore hard to isolate, total many millions. Collins officials claim a potential market for the C-System of some $200 million annually five years from now, but three years' revenues so far total only $35 million. Says one industry expert, "Some IBM salesmen have that sort of record." Yet much of Collins' soaring manufacturing and engineering overhead is related to the burden of the C-System.

What's more, in sharp contrast to its previous policy of expensing all its research and development costs, Collins in fiscal 1969 began deferring virtually all its C-System R&D (as well as substantial avionics research for the Lockheed L-1011, itself a troubled project). The total of these and other

brand, Ross Bros... scribe the change... accounting practic... the R&D involves... income for years... est Wish adds th... lies heavily on th... recover [those R&... tate revenues "W... he is satisfied wit... deferments]. Not... Why? Because t... such sophisticated... is much different... has been doing. I... experience, reputat... ganization of entro... IBM's equipment... one industry expert... in terms of qualit... thousand elves sta... it when it fails. C... an analyst acidly...

10

Troubled times

Thetwo problems which plagued Collins Radio at the end of the 1960s were not confined to one company. The latter half of the decade was very rough on many big defense contractors. Douglas Aircraft almost went under before merging with McDonnell Aircraft. Rolls-Royce Ltd., the maker of engines for Lockheed's new L-1011, declared bankruptcy. That situation strained the position of Lockheed, already reeling from $484 million in losses on four government contracts. Lockheed was in debt to 24 banks which refused to make any more loans to the aerospace giant unless the U.S. Government guaranteed them.

Government defense procurement dropped off as part of a deescalation plan for the Vietnam war. At the same time, space program expenditures were extended or postponed, and some were cancelled entirely.

Major manufacturers of commercial aviation products reduced employment extensively to allow themselves to weather the cutbacks.

Major markets for Collins' products declined, and the company was caught with commitments for major expenditures for plant expansion and product development in anticipation of future needs. Unable to cancel these commitments without incurring extensive cancellation charges, the company had to bear the damaging effects.

Collins had invested millions of dollars in research and development for the C-System, but sales lagged far behind anticipated levels. The practice of amortizing research and development costs the same as capital costs allowed earnings statements to appear in better shape than they actually were. Investors recognized the company's position, and Collins stock fell from its all-time high of over $100 per share to $50, opening the door for one of the most unusual take-over attempts in modern business history.

A sampling of newspaper articles from 1969 and 1970 points out the uneasy situation the company faced.

Little fish vs. a big fish
On March 24, 1969, H. Ross Perot stunned the business world by announcing that his small Dallas-based computer

concern, Electronic Data Systems Corporation ($8 million annual sales), intended to take over Collins Radio Company ($440 million annual sales).

Perot boasted that he was about to pull off the classic takeover. Using a common stock tender offer, he planned to swap his stock, selling at 300 times earnings, for the depressed shares of Collins. Electronic Data announced that it sought at least 1.4 million Collins common shares to add to the 75,000 it already held, to give it 51 percent of the Collins outstanding shares.

Electronic Data would exchange common stock having a market value of $65 a share for each Collins common share tendered with the maximum of 1.5 Electronic Data shares being swapped for each Collins share.

What followed was just the beginning of a struggle between two strong personalities — Arthur Collins and H. Ross Perot.

Two months earlier, Perot had approached Collins with merger plans. Perot noted that the value of his company was close to half a billion dollars — compared with the $150 million value of Collins stock. Collins was impressed with Perot, but he backed away from the merger when it became apparent that Perot would assume control of any combined company.

In 1971, the State of Iowa selected a Collins C-System for its statewide data network called TRACIS — for Traffic Records and Criminal Justice Information System. After touring Collins facilities, Governor Robert Ray held a news conference to publicize the State of Iowa-Collins Radio venture. Pictured from left: Marvin Selden, state comptroller; Governor Ray; William Roodhouse, Collins executive vice president; and Howard Walrath, Collins general services vice president.

Since his "friendly" method of merger did not work, Perot made the tender offer for the Collins stock. Top aides of Collins were concerned that the offer might force the company to combine with some other company to avoid an unfriendly takeover. But Mr. Collins opposed any hasty action. His initial reaction was that a takeover was impossible.

"We've ridden out a lot of rough storms in the last 35 years," Collins said, "and somehow we'll ride this one out, too."

But after three weeks of steady argument, company lawyers and others convinced him the threat was real.

Optimism characterized Electronic Data's headquarters. Collins Radio stock jumped to more than $60 a share following the announcement of the tender offer. High levels of trading indicated institutional investors were purchasing large amounts of Collins shares in anticipation of a successful offer. Two weeks after the announcement, Perot knew that ten institutional investors controlled more than one million shares of Collins common stock. Those investors held the key to victory or defeat.

Collins, aided by A. H. Gordon, chairman of Kidder, Peabody and Co., and a long-time friend of Arthur Collins, searched for potential "white knight" merger possibilities to thwart Electronic Data's takeover attempt. Exploratory talks were started with Harris-Intertype Corp., Burroughs Corp., Control Data, University Computing Co., and McDonnell Douglas.

A.H. Gordon with Arthur Collins. In addition to his chairmanship of Kidder, Peabody & Co., Gordon also served on the Collins Radio Co. Board of Directors.

Sam Wyly, president of University Computing, agreed to buy 300,000 shares of Collins common, but had to give it up when his own company's stock fell. Control Data ran into formidable Justice Department reservations to any merger with Collins.

These developments seemed to further Electronic Data's probability of success, but in the week following the tender announcement, Perot was not able to get Arthur Collins to meet with him to discuss the deal. Perot knew his chance of success would improve if he could get Collins and other board members to publicly accept the tender offer. The crucial question seemed to be what the big institutional shareholders would do if Mr. Collins walked out of any discussions.

During the second week following the offer, Collins publicly rejected the Electronic Data tender offer. In a special letter to stockholders and in a large ad in the April 3, 1969, *Wall Street Journal,* Arthur Collins stated the Electronic Data proposal was "hostile to the interests of the company and its shareholders," and that the Collins board of directors "has unanimously decided to oppose vigorously" the offer. Collins added: "Based on the latest fiscal year earnings and the over-the-counter bid quotations supplied by Electronic Data in its registration statement, the price-earnings ratio of its stock is in excess of 300 times."

Meanwhile, Collins looked around for other potential merger partners to save itself from Electronic Data. On April 8, 1969, two Collins vice presidents flew to Minneapolis to talk with Honeywell, Inc. But both sides saw Justice Department objections, and they couldn't agree on Mr. Collins' role in any merger. The Collins board ended merger talks with Honeywell April 19.

When an Electronic Data vice president heard the Collins-Honeywell talks had been called off, he was reported to have said, "The ball game is over," reasoning that time was running out for Collins.

But Mr. Collins held out. Four weeks after the disclosure of the offer, Chase Manhattan Bank, holder of 455,000 Collins shares, voiced its opposition. Chase and another New York bank, Morgan Guaranty Trust Co., were leery of swapping their shares for the high-multiple Electronic Data stock. They were, according to reports, waiting for Electronic Data to raise its offer to about $100 worth of stock for each Collins share. That presumably would have driven Collins stock up to approximately $85 a share, or high enough for the banks to unload their holdings at a profit.

Perot refused to sweeten the original offer. Chase Manhat-

This letter was mailed to Collins stockholders and appeared in the April 3, 1969, Wall Street Journal.

To the Stockholders of Collins Radio Company

Your Company's Board of Directors has unanimously decided to oppose vigorously the exchange offer proposed by Electronic Data Systems Corporation ("Electronic"). None of the Company's management or directors will accept the Electronic proposal.

We believe that the proposal is hostile to the interests of the Company and its stockholders. This belief is derived from the following considerations:

(1) Based on the latest fiscal earnings and the over-the-counter bid quotations supplied by Electronic in its registration statement, the price earnings ratio of its stock is in excess of 300 times. Of the outstanding Electronic shares, 91% are owned by nine officers and directors and additional shares are owned by other employees.

(2) You are being asked to make an exchange for stock which was first issued to the public about six months ago. The Electronic stock is not traded on the New York or any other stock exchange and there is no public information regarding the volume of trading.

(3) The latest reported fiscal year's sales of Electronic were only $7,666,000 as compared to Collins' $447,026,000 and its latest reported earnings per share for such period were 14¢ as compared to $4.44 for Collins.

(4) As set forth in the Electronic registration statement, Collins' shareholders accepting the offer would suffer very large dilution in earnings per share. For example, the earnings represented by each Collins share exchanged for 1.5 Electronic shares would be reduced from $4.44 to 25¢ if 20% of Collins' shareholders should exchange, and 93¢ even if 51% should exchange.

(5) Electronic has never declared any dividends and states that it does not expect to grant cash dividends in the near future. In the past twelve months, Collins' shareholders have received cash dividends of 80¢ per share.

(6) Acceptance of the Electronic exchange offer will be a taxable transaction to Collins' stockholders.

(7) Tenders to Electronic will be irrevocable and, therefore, Collins' stockholders lose control of their stock once the shares are tendered. Electronic, on the other hand, is not bound to accept any shares unless 51% or more are tendered.

(8) The Electronic proposal raises significant questions under the Federal AntiTrust laws, could have a serious adverse effect on the relations between the Company and its major customers (including the United States Government) and could jeopardize the personnel relationships within the Company which are vital to its continued technical achievements.

Your Board of Directors has great confidence in the future of Collins Radio Company, particularly in view of our recently announced intention of fully realizing the potential of our communication-oriented data systems as a major sector of business. The Company's research and development expenditures during the last twelve months for this and other future programs far exceed the total revenues of Electronic for its most recently reported fiscal year.

Your management has been evaluating a number of other transactions which, if consummated, might have an important effect on the current situation and the future of Collins Radio Company. We will keep you apprised of all pertinent developments in this regard.

Very truly yours,

Arthur A. Collins, President
By Order of the Board of Directors

March 28, 1969

tan and other large holders consolidated their opposition and sided with Collins. Electronic Data withdrew the tender offer before it was ever approved by the Securities and Exchange Commission.

An editorial in the May 11, 1969, *Cedar Rapids Gazette* reflected on the sequence of events:

"If *Wall Street Journal* reporter Norman Pearlstine's account of the recent abortive attempt to take over the Collins Radio Company is reasonably accurate — and we have no reason to doubt it — the people of Cedar Rapids and its surrounding area can add one more to many other reasons for being grateful to Arthur Collins. Evidently his cool determination and rugged spirit spared thousands of people in this community a great deal of prolonged anxiety, and possibly worse.

"We don't need to be financial sophisticates to sense how much Collins Radio means to all of us whose lives are rooted in this community. So it was not pleasant to watch from the sidelines an uncommonly audacious attempt to restructure an industry so important to the Cedar Rapids economy against the resistance of the man who built it."

Eighteen months later, Collins announced that it had initiated exploratory talks with TRW, Inc., about possible affiliation, but within two months, the talks were discontinued.

Rockwell enters

The critical cash flow condition at Collins continued to plague the company's operations in 1970. The company was in violation of cash conditions of several lenders' agreements, and sales continued to drop with the worldwide aerospace recession.

The Anamosa plant was closed in January, 1971, and the 240 employees were transferred to the Main Plant in Cedar Rapids.

The day following discontinuation of talks with TRW, it was announced that Collins and North American Rockwell Corporation had begun discussions on a possible significant investment in Collins. Two weeks later, on June 1, 1971, the managements of the two corporations had agreed on the terms of North American Rockwell's investment in Collins.

Subject to approval of respective boards of directors and Collins shareholders, North American Rockwell would purchase $35 million of a new issue of Collins convertible preferred stock, and would have warrants to purchase an additional $30 million of Collins common stock. The initial conversion and warrant exercise price was set at $18.50 per share, and the convertible preferred stock would give North American Rockwell the right to elect a majority of Collins' 13-member board of directors.

On June 10, the boards of directors for the two firms approved terms of the proposed investment. In a letter to Collins stockholders, Arthur Collins urged approval of the sale.

"The company's ability to continue its business clearly is dependent upon the receipt of substantial new financing. The proposed investment by North American Rockwell provides the needed additional capital and also does more . . . the participation by North American Rockwell's managerial talent on Collins' board of directors, while not necessarily assuring any improvement in Collins' present financial condition, will afford invaluable counsel in many aspects of our operations."

Pointing out that directors of both companies favored the proposal, Collins said its investment bankers also recommended approval of the agreement.

"Collins believes that if the proposed transaction with North American Rockwell is consummated, the proceeds . . . together with the restructuring of the bank debt . . . would enable Collins to meet its current financing requirements."

Collins stockholders approved the proposal on August 31, 1971. The agreement was consummated September 2, 1971, with the investment of $35 million in exchange for the agreed upon Collins shares and warrants.

North American Rockwell's original plan was to leave Collins management intact. But when the fiscal year 1971 loss of $46 million was followed by an $8 million first-quarter loss

Willard F. Rockwell, Jr. (left), chairman of the board of North American Rockwell, and Arthur A. Collins signed the agreement September 2, 1971, for the $35 million investment in Collins Radio.

175

in fiscal year 1972, Willard F. Rockwell, Jr., chairman of North American Rockwell, announced that Robert C. Wilson had been named president and chief executive officer of Collins, with Arthur Collins to continue as a member of the board. Other board members elected were R. L. Cattoi, senior vice president; W. C. Hubbard, vice president and controller; J. D. Nyquist, senior vice president; H. M. Passman, vice president; and W. W. Roodhouse, executive vice president.

After a meeting of the new board of directors on November 23, 1971, it was announced that Robert Wilson had been named new president and chief executive officer of Collins. At the stockholder's meeting, the election of directors representing Collins stockholders was postponed for a month. Seated at the head table were, from left, Donald Beall, Collins senior vice president for Finance and Administration; Willard Rockwell, Jr., newly-elected chairman of the Collins board; Robert Frost, Collins vice president and company secretary; and James Lenehan, Collins vice president of Telecommunications and Data Marketing.

When Collins was replaced as president and chairman of the board of the company he established, Roodhouse was traveling abroad. When he returned and discovered Collins had been replaced, Roodhouse submitted his resignation. Within a week, he returned to the firm convinced that the change in management was necessary for the company's survival.

On January 14, 1972, Collins announced his resignation from the board of directors. He announced the formation of a new corporation, Arthur A. Collins, Inc., to carry out system engineering studies in communications and computer fields.

Wilson, the new Collins president, had been with General Electric some 25 years before being tapped to head the commercial products group of North American Rockwell in 1969. At Rockwell, Wilson played a major role in recommending the investment in Collins. His recommendation was based largely on the fact that the two markets served by Collins — aviation and communications — were two of the very fast growing areas of the electronics industry.

"If you look at what's happening in communications, and what will happen over the new couple of decades, it is going to be almost an explosion on the total world base," Wilson said. He also believed that Collins Radio was rich in intangible assets such as its outstanding reputation with customers, market position, leadership in technology, and outstanding personnel.

"When things continued to look bad," Wilson said, "Rockwell management suggested that perhaps I ought to follow my judgment and come down and try to run it. So I did."

His first priority was to assure Collins personnel about the future of the business and the company. He also had to do a great deal of fence-mending with bankers and creditors.

Arthur Collins preferred the solitude of his laboratory to meeting with investors, creditors and customers. While he toiled in the lab, he sent subordinates to deal with the bankers.

Wilson, on the other hand, was described as the "hard-driving, outgoing, managerial type." He frequently held meetings with Collins officials in airports while he waited to change planes, talked freely with bankers, had breakfasts with local reporters, and made numerous speeches.

Robert C. Wilson

Wilson's plan

Upon arriving at Collins, Wilson sized up the situation and decided that all the things which led North American Rockwell to invest in Collins were there. However, he recognized the presence of several problems. Employee attitudes were poor because the company's future appeared questionable. The company showed a net loss of more than $40 million for the 1971 fiscal year, and things looked just as bad for 1972. Cash drain was projected to increase while orders continued to lag. The company needed strict fiscal controls, and many programs were in trouble. Wilson also recognized that the company needed better strategic planning. He felt that though these problems were deep-seated, they could be solved.

Wilson began his recovery plan with major cost-cutting policies. Capital expenditures were completely eliminated, and research and development funds were cut back to a level more in line with sales. Long-distance phone calls were reduced to a minimum, lights were turned out, use of copy machines was limited, duplication of research efforts was terminated, and 600,000-square-feet of leased space was vacated. Major cuts were made in personnel, with 2,000 engineers and administrators cut from the payroll. The company also improved its cash position through the sale and leaseback of $7.8 million of company-owned equipment.

Additional funds were received from a similar transaction of some of the company's production equipment.

The company changed its accounting practice from deferring development costs over product deliveries to expensing them as they occurred. A $36-million inventory write-down was made to get the value of such assets more in line with sales expectations. These two moves alone accounted for a major portion of the company's 1972 fiscal year loss of nearly $64 million. Wilson and his assistants conferred with Collins' lenders in 1971 and negotiated amended loan requirements to allow the company to get back in the black.

Coupled with the tight fiscal control was Wilson's major restructuring of the company's management in December, 1971. Nine organizational levels were reduced to five in some areas. The company was decentralized into four major operating groups: the Avionics and Telecommunications Group in Cedar Rapids; Telecommunications and Switching Systems in Dallas; the Special Telecommunication Group in Newport Beach; and International Operations headquartered in Dallas. Each group in turn was divided into operating divisions (totaling 15) which Wilson optimistically called profit centers. Each division concentrated on a single product area from marketing through engineering to production, to increase awareness of the bottom line.

Other major actions taken included re-evaluation on pricing policies and the establishment of new prices on many products, all with the approval of the Federal Wage and Price Board.

As part of the new organizational structure, marketing was emphasized as a critical factor for future company success.

The initial plan was to keep the company's focus on such traditional products as avionics and telecommunications

Under Wilson's plan, Collins was decentralized into four operating groups in 1971. Note that this chart does not reflect present groupings of operations.

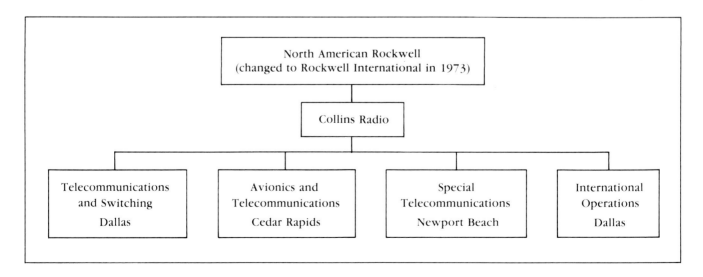

systems, to expand its development in the growing microwave business, and to shift emphasis away from computer and semiconductor activities where Collins was having a tough time with the competition.

The company's five-year plan, as expressed by Wilson, was to develop Collins into a solidly profitable and diversified growth company.

Part of the plan was to continue the development of international markets. In 1972, approximately one-third of total volume was achieved outside the United States. By 1977, the company expected that portion to be one-half.

In a presentation to security analysts in April, 1972, Wilson said he was confident the outlook for the future was good.

The turnaround

In March of 1972, the first 100 employees were called back to work. A March 17, 1972 editorial in the *Cedar Rapids Gazette* praised the development.

"There is every reason to conclude that negatives of paralytic gloom accumulating from the last two years are warranted no more on anybody's part."

The writer of the editorial was correct. Orders and sales for the first half of 1973 showed marked improvements of 66 percent and 46 percent, respectively, over the same period in 1972.

After reporting a $1.1 million profit for the first quarter of 1973, Willard F. Rockwell, Jr., chairman of the board of Collins Radio, extolled the efforts of Collins employees:

"In my 37 years in business I have never seen a turnaround as dramatic as this!"

From an operating loss of $17 million in 1972, Collins made a profit of $3 million in 1973. The company reduced its assets employed by 15 percent while sales increased by nearly 50 percent.

The profitable 1973 fiscal year led many investors to believe the merger of Collins Radio and North American Rockwell (renamed Rockwell International in February, 1973), was just a matter of time.

On August 20, 1973, Rockwell made a tender offer to purchase any and all shares of Collins common stock at $25 per share. Rockwell acquired 75 percent of Collins' outstanding common stock for approximately $57 million, and the merger of Collins into Rockwell was approved at a special meeting of Rockwell stockholders on November 2, 1973. Additional costs to acquire the balance of outstanding common stock and to consummate the merger came to approximately $19 million.

The merger of Collins Radio Company into Rockwell International was approved by Collins shareholders at a special shareholders meeting held in Cedar Rapids on November 2, 1973. Robert Wilson called the merger "The end of one phase in the development of Collins and the beginning of another which promises to be even more successful and dynamic than the first."

11
Jewel in the crown

P rogress may be too mild a word to describe the Collins about-face," a reporter wrote in the June 17, 1973, *Cedar Rapids Gazette.*

"Certainly the improvement in the economy has helped us a lot," said Clare Rice, senior vice president and general manager of the Collins Avionics Division. "We're in the aviation industry, and both the air transport sector and business aviation sector suffered in the recession for two or three years. But many other things helped too. We are now oriented to our markets, and our business teams are devoted to specific areas much more so than before. We are decentralized and I'm sure the focus we now have on various business areas is a significant factor in our financial performance."

The leaner Collins team continued its profitable growth in the mid-1970s and contributed significantly to the commercial and international business outlook for Rockwell International. Orders of about $500 million for 1974 represented an increase of 60 percent over the 1972 level; and more than 16 percent over 1973. Nearly 60 percent of sales were to commercial and international customers.

One aspect of the turnaround was a new marketing strategy for the C-System.

When financial analysts asked Wilson what he intended to do with the C-System, he replied, "You tell me what C-System means and I'll tell you."

That uncertainty did not last long. Wilson and Donald Beall, executive vice president of the Collins Radio Group, focused the C-System on a specialized but fast-growing segment of the communications market — voice and data switching. The C-System provided a good technical foundation for designing telephone exchanges and data switches for computer networks.

To get its foot in the door, the company turned to the airlines — long-time customers who were experiencing problems in data communications and telephone switching.

"The engineers from Collins really did their homework," said one airline official. "They came to see what we

A Gulfstream I company airplane sits beside the Collins hangar at the Cedar Rapids Airport. This airplane was sold in 1983. (See related article in this chapter.)

needed." The Collins engineering team worked with Continental Air Lines to design totally new systems to handle both telephone and data communications traffic for the airline's vital phone reservation and ticketing systems. Systems were later installed for Pan American and United.

Telephone companies offered automatic call distribution with their Star system, but because the Collins system offered so many more features, it was named the Galaxy system.

It was the first time such a sophisticated telephone system was used to solve the problem of evenly distributing large volumes of incoming calls to banks of telephones. It could also report on the number of calls coming in, how many callers were waiting, and how long they were waiting, among other features.

Once other companies saw the system working, more orders came in. By 1976, more than 25 Galaxy systems were on order, mostly for domestic airlines, hotel reservations systems, car rental companies, and credit authorization agencies.

The profit picture for other Collins markets also improved.

(In March, 1974, Robert Wilson resigned as president to become chairman of the board, president and chief executive officer of Memorex Corporation. Succeeding Wilson as president of the Collins Radio Group was Donald R. Beall, who had been executive vice president since December, 1971.)

Donald R. Beall, 1982 photo. Beall became president and chief operating officer of Rockwell International in 1979.

Upper
Employees present at the 1974 shipment of the first Galaxy system were, from left: Jim Miller, Gayne Ek, Jim Rise, Dean Thomas, Bob Abbott, Bob Bent, Harvey Lembke, Vivian Cerney, Bob Hirvela, Francis McMann, Clarence Marshall, John Pollpeter, Les Lauther and Bob McArthur.

Automatic call distribution systems were used by every major American airline and several foreign air carriers for computerized routing of telephone calls. Ozark Airlines installed a system at its regional reservation center in Peoria, Illinois. Ozark photo.

Avionics resurgence

A key market which returned to good health in the 1970s was aviation. Highlighting the growth was a 30 percent increase in avionics sales to general aviation and international customers between the 1973 and 1974 fiscal years.

In the early 1970s, a new integrated circuit process known as MOS (metal oxide semiconductor) became practical for avionics. The equivalent of hundreds (and even thousands) of transistors were processed on a single chip. MOS structures, smaller and requiring fewer process steps than the bipolar integrated circuits of the early 1960s, became the workhorses of the new avionics technology.

At the heart of this new era was the use of digital processing to fly the aircraft, manage fuel consumption, monitor engine performance, control communications and perform such navigational functions as storage and retrieval of waypoints, VOR-DME tuning and course and speed computations.

One application of the new technology was area navigation, or RNAV. A concept long recognized for its potential, RNAV provided direct point-to-point navigation off the established airways.

The first 40-year anniversary pin presented to an employee went to Katherine Horsfall in October 1973. Miss Horsfall joined Collins Radio Co. October 3, 1933 and served continuously in secretarial positions since that date. Presenting the pin were Clare Rice (left), who was named president of the Collins Avionics Group in 1977, and James Churchill, who succeeded Rice in 1981.

The new generation wide-body jet transports were the first to use advanced area navigation. *(See Chapter 8.)*

By installing these new digital systems aboard aircraft which were otherwise equipped with analog instruments, the aviation industry took the first step toward the all-digital age of the 1980s.

Collins also made technological strides in the business aviation field during the 1970s. The first of a new line of avionics was introduced in 1970 for business jets and twin-engine airplanes. Low Profile avionics featured remote-mounted boxes which were half the height of standard boxes and could be located in places previously too cramped for avionics. The height was the smallest of any remote box in the industry and allowed the installer, if he wished, to stack two boxes in one vertical space of the customary radio rack.

In the fall of 1973, Collins introduced its RNAV and control system for business aviation. The NCS-31 was a digital area navigation computer that also included an optional touch tune central control for all navigation and communication radios.

A Collins-owned Beech Duke criss-crossed the nation in 1974 and 1975 to demonstrate to business aviation customers the quality and versatility of the new avionics. Later tours of Europe and South America showed the world the reliability of the Low Profile Line.

Collins Pro Line was an avionics line designed for twin-engine airplanes and business jets — aircraft which most often would be flown by professional pilots. 1978 photo.

The Low Profile name was changed to Pro Line in 1975, and by the early 1980s, more than 100,000 units had been sold, making Pro Line one of the world's most successful product lines in business aviation.

In 1975, a new line of panel-mounted avionics for the single-engine and light twin-engine market was introduced. Micro Line products were based on the latest electronic display and microelectric circuits.

TACAN contract

One of the major Collins products during the 1970s and 1980s began with a significant contract award in August, 1973.

The Collins organization of Cedar Rapids was contracted to develop a new generation of TACAN equipment to meet new 252-channel requirements of the military. At that time, TACAN units were large and relatively unreliable compared to other equipment, and some of the technological advances in other avionics products had not been applied to TACAN.

Consequently, at the beginning of the 1970s, the U.S. Air Force established a list of features for a new system. The new TACAN had to be a smaller, lighter unit using advanced design techniques. It had to double the number of radio channels, add ranging capability, have high reliability and cost less than $10,000.

In April 1973, Collins was one of two companies each awarded a $1.5 million contract to develop and produce seven TACAN units for test and evaluation. The Collins team knew that if it won the competition, the Collins TACAN would likely be designated as standard equipment for the Air Force, and orders could total 10,000 units.

In July, 1975, the Air Force announced its decision. The team was awarded an initial production contract totaling $14 million for 1,000 systems, with options for an additional 7,000.

Reams of paper made up the TACAN proposal for the U.S. Air Force in 1974. Ed Baermann, Ann Bunting, Shirley King and Thad Kuenz are shown sorting the 28,000 sheets reproduced by the company's Reproduction Center.

Iowa Senator John Culver praised the Collins TACAN program on the floor of the U.S. Senate in 1978.

"The results to date have exceeded everyone's expectations," the senator told his colleagues. "In qualification tests, the Collins TACAN achieved a reliability of about 1,000 hours mean time between failures, which was double the original specifications. In field use, according to the most recently available data, the mean time between failures is more than 1,800 hours — or more than triple the requirement."

AN/ARN-118(V) TACAN

With the original Air Force TACAN award, the division pioneered the Reliability Improvement Warranty concept for military avionics. Under RIW, guaranteed field performance and a comprehensive maintenance program were provided to support equipment delivered to end customers.

The Collins Government Avionics Division achieved a milestone in 1979 when it shipped the 10,000th AN/ARN-118(V) TACAN, bringing the value of total orders to more than $125 million. The ARN-118 is one of the more successful products ever built by the division.

Reorganization and expansion

By the summer of 1974, employment in Cedar Rapids was climbing at a rate of 100 persons each week as the backlog of orders continued to increase.

Business Week magazine quoted Willard F. Rockwell, chairman of the board of Rockwell International, as saying the former Collins Radio Co. was "the jewel in the crown" of the Rockwell organization.

In conjunction with its decentralization efforts, Rockwell management organized the Cedar Rapids Collins operations into five distinct divisions in 1977.

The Collins Telecommunications Products Division (CTPD) was chartered to manufacture radio communication products.

The Collins Communications Switching Systems Division handled automatic call distribution systems.

The three avionics divisions — Air Transport, General Aviation, and Government — comprised the Collins Avionics Group. Clare Rice was named president of the Collins Avionics Group.

In June, 1974, the company leased a manufacturing plant in Melbourne, Florida, while construction began on a new, larger building in Florida. Located on that state's east coast near Cape Canaveral and the Kennedy Space Center, Melbourne offered a new source of trained electronic personnel close to a hub of aerospace activity.

In 1977, a new 40,000-square-foot facility was dedicated in Melbourne for the Collins General Aviation Division.

Also in 1977, four expansions in Iowa were announced.

A mechanical assembly plant employing about 40 persons opened in Manchester for the Collins Air Transport Division.

In Anamosa, the Collins Telecommunications Products Division opened a service center in the building used by Collins as a manufacturing plant from 1955 until 1971.

A new 42,000-square-foot facility opened in Mason City for inspecting purchased parts and fabricating plastic parts for Collins avionics products.

The new Melbourne, Florida, plant was dedicated in 1977.

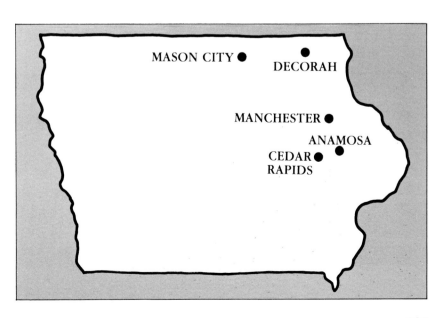

The Advanced Technology and Engineering Center (Building 124) in Cedar Rapids, as viewed from the east.

In Cedar Rapids, Collins Communications Switching Systems Division began construction of a 110,000-square-foot building for laboratories, manufacturing, warehousing and office space on a 10-acre site near the C Avenue complex.

The following year, Collins Air Transport Division opened its new 7,500-square-foot facility in Decorah, Iowa.

Expansion continued in Cedar Rapids in 1978. Administrative offices of CTPD were moved to leased space in the Life Investors Inc. building, and more than 100 of the division's employees occupied the second and fourth floors of the Iowa-Illinois Gas and Electric Co. building. The company's Graphic Services Department moved into leased space in the former Vigortone Products headquarters on Blairs Ferry Road.

In 1979, Rockwell purchased Wescom, a Downers Grove, Illinois-based company which had developed a private branch exchange (PBX) to integrate various office functions such as telephones and computers. Wescom was placed in the Collins Communications Switching Systems Division. (In 1983, Rockwell withdrew from the PBX business and emphasis was placed on updating Galaxy products, including a system for telephone company directory assistance.)

"Advanced technology and engineering capability is the heart of design and development of new avionics products and systems for the markets we serve," Rice said in announcing a new expansion. "And these markets are growing rapidly. Consequently, we've run out of available laboratory and office space."

In late 1979 and through the spring of 1980, about 800 avionics engineering employees moved into a new 200,000-square-foot engineering and research facility at the C Avenue complex in Cedar Rapids (Building 124).

A new facility for automated warehousing and assembly for CTPD was opened in Salt Lake City, Utah, in 1979.

Another expansion was made in 1980. Two Rockwell divisions with similar customer interests — the Collins Government Avionics Division of Cedar Rapids and the Missile Systems Division of Columbus, Ohio — opened a 75,000-square-foot plant near Atlanta, Georgia, to produce a variety of electronic assemblies.

Major contracts

During the late 1970s, several large contracts were awarded to the Collins divisions in Cedar Rapids, as the telecommunications and aviation industries strengthened.

Among them were the new standard U.S. Air Force transceiver, the AN/ARC-186(V); a $48 million avionics package for the U.S. Coast Guard's Medium Range Surveillance (MRS) aircraft; a Short Range Recovery (SRR) helicopter avionics package for the U.S. Coast Guard; and a new high frequency radio for about half the U.S. Air Force's aircraft (ARC-190).

Jack Cosgrove (right), vice president and general manager of Collins Telecommunications Products Division, accepts a trophy model of an early ARC-159 radio from Tom Wilford, division manufacturing manager. The event marked the 5,000th such unit delivered to customers. 1977 photo.

The atrium of Building 124 in Cedar Rapids serves as a reception area for the Avionics Group.

191

A 34-year-old helicopter pilot involved in a mid-air collision over a major metropolitan area, credited the Collins autopilot system installed in his aircraft with saving his life.

"There's no doubt about it, none whatsoever in my mind," says Edward Gabryszewski of Sterling Heights, Michigan. "Without the Collins autopilot, I'd probably be dead right now."

On March 22, 1982, Gabryszewski, a pilot for WJBK-TV (CBS) in Detroit, dropped off a news crew at the television station and took off for nearby Berz-Macomb Airport to secure his helicopter for the night.

After clearing the towers and tall buildings of downtown Detroit, he activated the Collins APS-841H autopilot in the Bell JetRanger III helicopter and started to relax.

Thirty seconds later, by his own estimation, Gabryszewski was knocked unconscious by what he describes as "a loud explosion." The "explosion," he would learn at the end of his ordeal, was a five-pound mallard duck crashing through the JetRanger's windscreen.

In the collision, the mallard "took out two-thirds of the windscreen on the pilot's side and struck me square in the face," Gabryszewski recounted. "The force of the impact broke my nose but the duck, for the instant it was on my face, shielded my eyes from the flying plexiglass that followed it through the hole."

Gabryszewski was unconscious for 90 seconds. Revived by the cold wind blowing through the JetRanger's shattered windscreen, he found himself still cruising at 700 feet and 110 knots over Detroit.

"When I came to, I was still in my harness, slumped over the co-pilot's seat. I tried to sit up. But as I did, I grabbed the cyclic and accidentally disengaged the autopilot. The chopper started to climb immediately and began to do an inverted roll to the right. I was only semi-conscious, but I could feel what was going on, so I started fighting like hell to regain control. Then I realized I could get some help. I punched up the autopilot again and let go of the cyclic. The chopper came back around. I leaned back and cleared by head."

Gabryszewski managed to safely land the helicopter at a nearby airport — Big Beaver — and was joined there minutes later by a concerned police helicopter pilot. It was the latter who discovered the cause of the "explosion," lying atop a videotape recorder in the JetRanger's rear seat.

Now fully recovered from his injuries, Gabryszewski considers himself "very fortunate, very lucky. I still can't thank Collins and my president enough . . . for my life."

It was Kenneth Bagwell, president of Storer Broadcasting Co. of Miami, which owns WJBK, who authorized installation of the APS-841H at Gabryszewski's request.

Pilot Ed Gabryszewski poses with five-pound mallard duck that crashed through the windscreen of the helicopter he was flying over Detroit. 1982 photo.

192

The first active control system, for the Lockheed L-1011-500 jetliner, was delivered in 1979. The system, combined with nine extra feet of wing span, was designed to reduce drag, fuel consumption, and structural wing loads. The application was the first commercial use of active controls technology and remained the only such system in use by 1983.

The commitment to America's space program continued in the 1980s when Collins navigation systems were provided for the Space Shuttle.

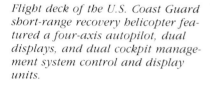

Flight deck of the U.S. Coast Guard short-range recovery helicopter featured a four-axis autopilot, dual displays, and dual cockpit management system control and display units.

The advanced Collins flight management system (FMS-90) is used to program automatic navigation on board the aircraft, and can control several other avionics systems. 1981 photo.

New navigation equipment

Collins produced one of the earliest automatic navigation systems, the ANS-70, for the large commercial jets in the early 1970s, but its large size and price tag weren't suited to the needs of smaller business aviation aircraft.

In September, 1979, Rockwell International purchased Communications Components Corporation, a Costa Mesa, California-based electronics firm. CCC's product line consisted of simple antennas and highly sophisticated long-range navigation radios. The acquisition was made to expand the Collins general aviation avionics product line.

Collins engineers took the long-range navigation idea a step further by adding complete flight management capability and calling it the FMS-90.

So many cockpit functions could be controlled by the FMS-90 that when the system was introduced at the 1980 National Business Aircraft Association convention, one aviation writer asked, "Can it brew coffee?"

In July, 1979, the Collins Government Avionics Division received a $68 million contract for a totally new type of navigation equipment — the largest developmental contract Collins had received since Project Apollo.

The new Navstar Global Positioning System (GPS) was viewed as the navigation system for the future, intended to ultimately replace many of the navigation methods used by aircraft, ships and land vehicles.

The system, when fully implemented in the late 1980s, would consist of three segments.

The space segment was to be made up of 18 satellites operating in three separate orbits.

The ground control segment would consist of stations to track the satellites, monitor their operation and make corrections to insure accuracy.

Navstar Global Positioning System equipment developed by the Collins Government Avionics Division.

The user segment, to include Collins-developed equipment, would receive the satellites' signals and convert them into a precise position readout. The system was to be so accurate that a pilot, the captain of a ship, or even a foot soldier carrying GPS equipment would be able to determine, in three dimensions, his location anywhere on Earth within a few meters.

After nearly a decade of program involvement, the Collins Government Avionics Division decided to demonstrate the potential of the system for civil users. Collins engineers placed GPS equipment in a Rockwell Sabreliner business jet in May, 1983, and made the first transatlantic flight using signals from Navstar satellites for navigation. The Collins crew landed at Le Bourget Airport, site of the Paris Air Show, and then relied on precise satellite positioning data to taxi the aircraft within eight meters of a predetermined parking point.

Collins engineers also worked on a development contract with General Motors to install the sophisticated GPS navigation equipment in automobiles.

The Collins Government Avionics Division was one of two manufacturers vying for the full-scale GPS user equipment production contract, expected in 1984.

Picture tubes in the cockpit

Television picture tubes — cathode ray tubes (CRTs) — have been around since the 1940s, but their use in aviation was limited for many years. The early tubes were heavy and required complex circuitry. Their biggest drawback was a lack of picture brightness.

The 1950s brought brighter CRTs, and single-color displays began to be used in cockpit weather radars. Advances in tube design and integrated circuitry through the 1960s, plus the advent of color displays, finally made CRTs economical and practical for broader applications in aviation.

By the early 1970s, Collins engineers were drawing on their expertise in flight display technology to begin experimenting with CRTs as primary flight instruments — taking the place of electromechanical instruments and their many moving parts.

For the new flight instrument CRTs, Collins engineers chose a unique method of display using shadow mask tubes. A shadow mask tube allows a full-color presentation and a bright, crisp picture. Although the principle had been applied to home color television sets, no avionics manufacturer had been able to make a shadow mask tube rugged enough to reliably withstand the vibrations of flight — until the Collins Air Transport Division and its tube supplier developed the technology.

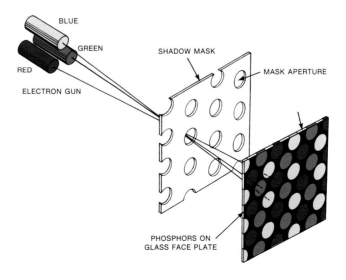

Principle of shadow mask color cathode ray tube.

The division was the only avionics manufacturer to develop shadow mask tube technology, but the gamble paid off in 1978 when the Boeing Commercial Airplane Company chose Collins systems for its new-generation airliners.

For the Boeing 757 and 767, two systems using Collins color CRTs were ordered, both representing a radical departure from conventional electromechanical instruments and sparking a revolution in aircraft flight deck design. Instead of intricate moving parts, the electronic flight instruments presented crisp images on a CRT screen. By turning a switch, the pilot could change the type of display on the instrument.

With these systems, a new era of information access and aircraft system management was opened to the flight crew.

The Boeing 757 and 767 flight decks feature Collins electronic flight instruments, electronic engine indication instruments, digital autopilots and other modern systems. Boeing photo.

Boeing 767 and 757 in flight. Boeing photo.

The information was presented in full-color, sunlight-readable displays directly in front of the pilot and co-pilot.

Never before had such a massive amount of data been available for selection by the crew. The technological task facing Collins engineers was to simplify the displayed information in order to reduce cockpit workload and minimize training for pilots learning to fly the new aircraft.

Collins engineers met this challenge by providing flight-critical data in meaningful formats similar to what the pilots were accustomed to seeing on their old instruments. The system could automatically display critical information while in flight. Additional information was available with the push of a button.

The first electronic flight instrument system certified by the FAA was the Collins EFIS for the Boeing 767 in July, 1982.

Digital electronics

Not only was it the first FAA-certified use of CRTs as primary flight instruments, the 767 was also the first completely "digital" aircraft, a technological step just as significant to the aviation industry.

In switching to digital computer-based avionics systems, the aviation industry was removing its 40-year-old "analog" jacket and ordering a new tailor-made "digital" suit.

The contract which led to the first completely digital avionics systems had its origin in the early 1970s.

"We analyzed what we could do with the technology," said Jim Churchill, then vice president and general manager

Digital avionics were demonstrated to the world air transport aviation community in April 1980, when the Collins Air Transport Division hosted a three-day symposium in Cedar Rapids. Nearly 200 industry personnel attended, representing airlines, airframe manufacturers and industry organizations.

of the Collins Air Transport Division, "and went after the 767 business before Boeing even had a name for it. But we knew they were coming with a new family."

(In March, 1981, Churchill succeeded Rice as president of the Avionics Group, making him Rockwell's senior executive in Cedar Rapids. Rice was appointed vice president of marketing and assistant to the president for Rockwell's Commercial Electronics Operations, and retired in 1983.)

When the division assumed the task of designing the new system, it was more than just a technological challenge. Another hurdle was the industry-wide competition.

At the conclusion of the contract awards, the Collins Air Transport Division had won three of the first four major avionics systems for the 767 and 757. They were the flight control system, electronic flight instruments system (EFIS), and the engine indication and crew alerting system (EICAS).

The Boeing 767 entered commercial service with United Air Lines in September, 1982. British Airways and Eastern Airlines introduced the 757 early in 1983. A European consortium of manufacturers — Airbus Industrie — also introduced new digital jetliners featuring many Collins digital units.

The digital concept was adopted by new-generation aircraft in the business aviation and regional airline markets as well.

In the summer of 1981, Collins equipment was selected for the Saab-Fairchild 340, the Short Brothers 360, and Embraer's EMB-120 *Brasilia*. Other turboprop and business jet contracts followed as the Collins General Aviation Division led the way for the business and commuter aviation conversion to digital avionics.

The first all-digital business and commuter-class aircraft was the Saab-Fairchild SF-340, which features Collins avoinics as standard equipment. Saab-Fairchild photo.

In September, 1982, the first CRT flight instrument for general aviation — a Collins EHSI-74 — was certified aboard a Commander 690 turboprop.

In January, 1983, an entirely new line of digital radios for business, regional airline and military aircraft — Collins Pro Line II — was introduced by the Collins General Aviation Division.

A new product introduced in 1983 by the Collins Air Transport Division was a digital color weather radar for jetliners which could detect turbulence in precipitation — a first in the industry.

An important program for the Collins Government Avionics Division in the early 1980s was an advanced system for the U.S. Air Force that could display friendly and enemy aircraft, navigation checkpoints, hostile surface-to-air missile sites and airfields. The program was called Joint Tactical Information Distribution System (JTIDS).

The portfolio of new products at the Collins Telecommunications Products Division included a communications processor (SELSCAN) that automatically scanned a number of frequencies, determined their availability and quality, and established a confirmed link on the best available channel.

In the spring of 1983, veteran Collins Flight Operations pilot Chuck Hall bade farewell to a very special lady. He did so with a lump in his throat and a pause to reflect upon the many hours — over 4,500 — he had shared with her.

"She's taken me all over the world and never let me down," he recalled. "She's just like an old brood cow — gentle. There's not a mean bone in her body."

She was readily recognizable as the Collins Gulfstream I, or G-1 — the 144th twin turboprop to roll off the old Grumman Aircraft Engineering Corp. production line in Bethpage, Long Island, New York.

That was in February 1965. In mid-March of 1983, she was ferried to Columbus, Indiana, for delivery to the Seven-Bar Flying Service — only the second owner in her 18 years.

Throughout the prime of her life, No. 144 covered the skies between Cedar Rapids and Dallas (Addison Field), shuttling employees to and from Collins engineering and manufacturing facilities in the two cities. For a number of years, she performed similar duties on a Dallas-Newport Beach, California, route.

Among her countless passengers were top Collins and Rockwell executives — Arthur A. Collins, W.W. (Bill) Roodhouse, Robert C. Wilson, Donald R. Beall, Martin D. (Skip) Walker, Clare I. Rice, James L. Churchill — who "enjoyed her comfort on a flight tailored to the businessman," said Hall.

During the days of the Apollo lunar landing program, No. 144 frequently was called upon to transport the families of American astronauts from Houston to Cape Canaveral.

The Collins G-1 hosted some well-known entertainers, too. On separate occasions, John Wayne and Bob Hope were given ground demonstrations of Collins systems aboard the aircraft.

Down through the years, the big twin's most important role has been that of a flying testbed and customer demonstrator for major Collins avionics systems designed and developed in Cedar Rapids.

Customer demonstration tours took the G-1 to countries throughout the world — 21 in all — including Canada, Mexico, Great Britain, Scotland, Sweden, France, Belgium, West Germany, Denmark, Italy, Spain, Por-

By the late 1960s, the fleet of Collins aircraft included a Beech Twin and three Grumman Gulfstream I turboprops.

tugal, Greenland and Iceland. And she appeared for many years at the now-defunct Reading (Pa.) Air Show, and the annual National Business Aircraft Association (NBAA) meeting and convention.

Altogether, No. 144 compiled an impressive list of statistics in her years under the Collins and Rockwell banners, including:

19,800 accident-free flight hours (92 hours per month), a total of 5,702,400 miles — equivalent to nearly 12 round-trip flights to the moon.

8,000 landings, during which the aircraft used 40 sets of tires.

Six major overhauls of the original set of Rolls Royce Dart Mark 529-8X turboprop engines which burned fuel at the rate of 220 gallons per hour and consumed a total of 4,356,000 gallons of kerosene.

She became the first G-1 in Grumman (now Gulfstream Aerospace Corp.) history to reach the 20,000-hour-inspection plateau.

For all of her storied history, No. 144 has not been the only G-1 to grace the Collins hangar, but she does represent the lone example of a new G-1 to spend a near full life based in Cedar Rapids.

Over the years, the company has owned five G-1s, but no more than three at any one time.

One of those — No. 163 — was destroyed July 11, 1975, at Addison in one of the first major aviation accidents attributed to wind shear. The quick thinking and intuitive responses of Capt. Dave Selzer and co-pilot Dave Tschudi saved not only their own lives, but seven others aboard the craft. Moreover, all nine emerged from the incident without serious injury.

The good fortune of the passengers and crew was due in part, said Hall, to the structural integrity of "any" airplane built by the 'Grumman Iron Works' — a phrase coined by World War II pilots of LeRoy Grumman's famed 'Cat' series of planes (Wildcat, Hellcat, Tigercat, Bearcat) which survived more than their share of hard landings on such surfaces as aircraft carrier flight decks.

None will be remembered quite like the first — No. 144. From those who most often strapped themselves into her left seat — Harvey Hop, Dick Johnson, Clayt Lander, Selzer, Hall, "Jug" Hiser and Gil Strait — to the thousands of passengers who appreciated her big-cabin comfort and other airliner-like amenities, she may always be known as the 'Queen of the Fleet.'

And she will be missed.

"She was the first big airplane I ever flew," said Hall. "I cut my teeth on her."

With Johnson, pilot Barry Brown and mechanic Randy Weyer, Hall cut his teeth on trans-Atlantic flying, too, ferrying the big turboprop from Cedar Rapids to Toulouse, France, for customer demonstration of new digital air transport avionics in 1979.

Now the role of avionics testbed, customer demonstrator and employee shuttle will fall to a new generation. "She's being replaced by smaller, more fuel-efficient aircraft," explained Hall, who likened the sale to "the shooting of an old horse."

Said he, "She was a peach of an airplane, and a true airplane — one that would tell you when she was going to do something before she did it.

"She will not soon be forgotten."

Recession effect

In the spring of 1980, the economic recession, which was ravaging the automobile and housing industries, made its presence felt at the Collins divisions in Cedar Rapids.

In particular, the air transport and general aviation markets were suffering from business slowdowns. Deregulation in 1978 meant major changes in the way the airlines conducted business, and many airline procurement programs were disrupted.

Consumer spending slowed to a crawl because of tight money supplies and high interest rates, which led to smaller corporate profits. Many companies, in turn, postponed or cancelled plans for purchases of business aircraft and the avionics that went with them.

In the early 1980s, employment cutbacks were made in the Cedar Rapids divisions to reduce operating costs as the management team attempted to cope with stagnant economic conditions.

Amid rumors that Collins operations were to be pulled out of the city, management assured employees that the Rockwell International divisions were "deeply committed to Cedar Rapids, which continues to be our center of excellence for engineering and manufacturing."

Through interactive terminals, such as this one operated by Cindy Meihost, Cedar Rapids-based engineers have direct access to the high-speed computing facilities of Rockwell's Information Systems Center, in addition to local processing systems.

However, Clare Rice and Jack Cosgrove (CTPD vice president and general manager) each said times ahead would be tough. More cost-cutting measures would be taken to keep the company competitive in its markets.

Automated equipment is used to test circuit boards before they are integrated into final products. Mary Taylor is pictured operating the machine.

Collins Air Transport Division Process Center employs advanced automatic component insertion, wave solder, wash, test and conformal coating techniques to produce multilayer circuit boards.

Those measures included taking a more involved role with employee health care costs. In January, 1981, the company opened its own pharmacy as an added service for employees and families, and to cut the company's health insurance costs.

"We are well postured so that if the economy turns, and we can hold our costs in line, we're going to enjoy a tremendous gain and experience prosperity," Churchill said in a 1983 address to Avionics Group managers.

"We've got to be better, just simply better. We need to give more value for the dollar, more product features, and we've got to provide better service. That's where we're trying to spend our money today . . ."

Change in the landscape brought about by the Collins divisions of Rockwell International can be seen by comparing this view with the photograph on page 98. Building 120, headquarters for Collins Telecommunications Products Division, lies to the left of C Avenue. Across the street to the right is headquarters for the Avionics Group. The light area at top center is Main Plant — the first facility constructed by Collins Radio Company. 1983 photo.

"We are just in the kindergarten
of uncovering things:
and there is no down curve
in science."

Charles Franklin Kettering

Arthur A. Collins

Arthur A. Collins, founder of Collins Radio Company, has been called a rare man of greatness, a complex but shy person, who continually has his sights not on the epicenter, but beyond the horizon of technology.

He broke barriers of conventional knowledge and made routine a pattern of scientific advancement. For him and the company he founded and directed for 40 years, work brought many personal rewards, but it was the technical breakthrough and total utilization of technology which provided the greatest motivation.

Collins attended Cedar Rapids public schools, Amherst College in Amherst, Massachusetts in 1927, Coe College in Cedar Rapids for special courses, and the University of Iowa for advanced studies in physics.

He received an honorary doctor of science degree from Coe College in 1954, an honorary doctorate from the Polytechnic Institute of Brooklyn in 1968, an honorary doctor of engineering degree from Southern Methodist University in 1970, and an honorary doctor of science degree from Mount Mercy College in Cedar Rapids in 1974.

From 1945 through 1951, Mr. Collins served as a director of Coe College. He was a director of the Graduate Research Center of the Southwest, Dallas, from 1962 to 1969, and served on the board of directors of the Herbert Hoover Foundation.

He was a member of the International Sponsors Committee of the Robert Hutchings Goddard Library Program, Clark University, Worcester, Massachusetts.

Mr. Collins belongs to the Institute of Electrical and Electronic Engineers, the Navy League of the United States, the American Ordnance Association, the Armed Forces Communications and Electronics Association, and was a member of the Cedar Valley Amateur Radio Club.

He received the Secretary of the Navy's Distinguished Public Service Award Citation in 1962, the Iowa Broadcasters Association Distinguished Service Award in 1966, was elected to the National Academy of Engineering in 1968, received the Armed Forces Communications and Electronics Association's David Sarnoff Award in 1979, and the Electronics Industries Association's Medal of Honor in 1980.

After leaving Collins Radio in 1972, he formed a new firm, Arthur A. Collins, Inc., based in Dallas, to carry out systems engineering studies in the communications and computer fields.

He is married to Mary Margaret (Meis), and was formerly married to Margaret Van Dyke, who died in 1955. He has four children.

Fifty years represents a brief time period when compared to almost five millenia of recorded history. However, the significance of such a period should be measured by what changes took place, and what effect those years are likely to have on the future.

From the earliest days of shortwave transmitters to today's satellite navigation, flight management systems and electronic counter-counter measures, the Collins name has been a leader with distinctive quality and state-of-the-art technology.

The Collins history is filled with tales of technological wizardry, unusual twists of fate, dogged determination, and amazing resiliency.

Fifty years of Collins products

NOTE: This chart is intended to give a general impression of Collins products introduced and in production in Cedar Rapids in the company's 50-year history. It is neither a complete nor wholly accurate list. The information was compiled from several previously published lists from the Collins divisions, and each had its own standards for compilation.

Beginning dates are probably more accurate than end dates. An end date of 1983 signifies that the particular product is either still in production or serviced and supported by Collins personnel.

Type No.	Description	
4A	20W amateur CW transmitter (amateur)	1933
300A	200W shortwave transmitter (broadcast)	1933-1935
32B	25W CW transmitter (amateur)	1934
45A	40W phone, 125W CW amateur transmitter	1933-1934
300E,F	100W & 250W broadcast transmitters	1933-1934
300C	250W broadcast transmitter	1933-1935
202A	600W 1.5 to 30 mcs commercial transmitter	1933-1934
20D,C	1 kW broadcast transmitter	1934-1936
32F	25W phone transmitter (amateur)	1934
20F	1 kW communications transmitter	1936-1938
21D	5 kW grid-mod broadcast transmitter	1936-1939
150A,B,C	50-200W commercial transmitter	1937-1939
600A	amateur 600W CW, 250W phone	1937-1939
30FX	amateur transmitter, 200W CW, 70W phone	1937-1938
30FXA,B	amateur 200W phone	1937-1939
18m-1-5	portable ground transceiver, 10W	1937-1940
32RA	HF 50W transmitter	1937-1943
20K	1 kW broadcast transmitter	1938
21A	5 kW plate-mod broadcast transmitter	1938-1940
236A	20-40 mcs, 500-1,000W broadcast transmitter	1938-1940
32G	amateur 40W phone & CW transmitter	1938-1940
30J	amateur 250W phone & CW transmitter	1938-1941
150S	commercial 250W phone & CW transmitter	1938-1940
231B,C	1 kW autotuned HF transmitter	1939-1940
16F6	HF autotuned transmitter	1939-1940
30FXC	amateur 200W transmitter (10 meterband)	1939-1940
231D-1 thru 20	3 kW, 2-18 mcs, HF transmitter	1940, 1944-1949
17D,F	first airborne autotuned transmitter	1940-1941
TCS	50Q 2-12 mcs transmitter, 40W CW	1940-1944
TCS	51Q 2-12 mcs manually-tuned receiver	1940-1944
TDO	Navy 300W phone, 500W CW, 2-18 mcs autotuned transmitter	1941-1945
TDH, 1 to 4	3 kW phone, 5 kW CW, 2-18 mcs autotuned transmitter	1941-1946
AN/ART-13	airborne autotuned 100W transmitter	1941-1946

Type No.	Description	
TCZ	ground version of ART-13	1942-1946
AN/ARC-2	2-9 mcs, autotuned 30W airborne transceiver	1944-1946
18S	commercial airborne HF transceiver	1945-1947
300G	250W broadcast transmitter	1945-1947
51M-1	VHF fixed tuned ground station receiver	1945-1947
20T	1 kW broadcast transmitter	1945-1947
51J-1	communications receiver	1945-1948
30K	amateur 500W transmitter	1945-1948
	Resnatron development	1946-1952
	400 mcs Transhorizon propagation studies	1946-1953
51N-1	fixed tuned HF receiver	1946
32V-1	150W amateur transmitter	1946-1948
731A	250W FM broadcast transmitter	1946-1948
732A	1 kW FM broadcast transmitter	1946-1948
733A	3 kW FM broadcast transmitter	1946-1948
737A	5 kW FM broadcast transmitter	1946-1948
734A	10 kW FM broadcast transmitter	1946-1949
21B	5 kW AM broadcast transmitter	1946-1948
21L	10 kW AM broadcast transmitter	1946-1948
3000A-1	VHF communications package	1946-1948
AN/ARC-27	airborne 1750-channel UHF 10W transceiver	1946-1952
	mechanical filter development	1947-1956
75A-1	amateur double conversion receiver	1947-1949
AN/FRT-5	15 kW, 4-26 mcs CW transmitter	1947-1950
AN/FRT-6	40 kW, 4-26 mcs CW transmitter	1947-1951
51M-3	VHF fixed tuned receiver	1947
51N-2	HF fixed tuned receiver	1947-1948
17L-1	communications transmitter	1947-1949
17L-2	communications transmitter	1947-1949
51R-1	nav/comm receiver	1947-1949
51R-2	nav/comm receiver	1947-1949
51N-4	HF fixed tuned FSK receiver	1948-1950
706A-2	diversity teletype converter	1948-1950
51N-3	CODAN fixed tuned HF receiver	1948-1950
KWS-1	HF transmitter	1948-1966
32V-2	150W amateur transmitter	1949-1950
75A-2	amateur receiver	1949-1951
AN/GRC-27	ground station UHF transceiver	1949-1954
51J-2	communications receiver	1949
KW-1	1 kW amateur transmitter	1949-1950
	predicted wave radio teletype development	1949-1957
207-B-1	40 kW, 4-26 mcs AM transmitter	1950-1951
R-391	autotuned 0.5-32 mcs Signal Corps receiver	1950-1953
R-389	LF Signal Corps receiver	1950-1953
R-390	0.5-32 mcs Signal Corps receiver	1950-1954

Fifty years of Collins products

Type No.	Description	
51J-3	communications receiver	1950-1951
AN/GRC-19	autotuned transceiver 100W transmitter	1950-1955
51N-5	fixed tuned HF FSK receiver	1951-1952
	VHF long-range propagation studies	1951-1955
75A-2	amateur receiver with mechanical filters	1951-1952
207A-1	15 kW, 4-26 mcs AM transmitter	1951-1953
51R-3	nav/comm receiver	1951
51X-1	nav/comm receiver	1952
AN/FRT-22	30 kW SSB, 4-26 mcs transmitter	1952-1954
AN/FRT-26	10 kW SSB, 4-26 mcs transmitter	1952-1954
430 series	HF transmitters (12 variations)	1952-1954
618S	airborne 144-channel, 100W HF transceiver	1952-1954
21E,M	5 & 10 kW broadcast transmitters	1952-1954
300J,550A	100W to 1 kW broadcast transmitters	1952-1954
AN/FRR-33	diversity FSK teletype receiving set	1952-1954
AN/FRT-24	special 1 kW 430-series transmitter (Navy)	1952-1954
	microwave relay communication development	1952-1954
	24-channel voice multiplex development	1952-1954
242F2,3	VHF 108-152 mcs fixed tuned transmitters (50-200W)	1952-1953
	SSB equipment study program	1952-1953
51J-4	communications receiver w/mechanical filters	1952-1954
	C.R.-Dallas PWRT tests	1952-1953
51M-6	VHF fixed frequency receiver	1952-1953
T-276	500W, 1.75-32 mcs SSB transmitter development	1953-1955
OA-252	4 kW SSB transmitter with T-276 exciter	1953-1955
240C-1	1 kW 225-1000 mcs FM transmitter	1953-1954
AN/ARC-52	VHF airborne comm	1953-1969
AN/VRC-24	UHF vehicular comm	1953-1969
	Cedar Rapids-Lamar 960 mcs propagation study	1954-1955
AN/ARC-51	UHF airborne comm	1954-1974
205G-1	20 kW, 20-50 mcs transmitter development	1954-1955
	Scattergood Project for DEW Line: VHF duplex	1954-1955
	4-channel time division PWRT for DEW Line	1954-1955
30G-1	700-985 mcs FM receiver	1954-1955
310K-1	700-985 mcs FM exciter	1954-1955
240E-1	1 kW 700-1000 mcs Klystron power amplifier	1955
	DEW Line lateral communication system	1955
	120-channel multiplex development	1955
	common carrier and STL-TV microwave development	1955
	Continental-Sinclair microwave contract	1955
	Signal Corps PWRT tests	1955
	Kineplex (new type of PWRT) development	1955
51V-3	glideslope receiver	1955-1978
240D-1	10 kW UHF Klystron transmitter	1955
	AF SSB system contract (Project Birdcall)	1955

Type No.	Description	
	Bureau of Ships high capacity comm system	1955
	Signal Corps scatter propagation study	1955
51R-4	nav/comm receiver	1955
51X-2	nav/comm receiver	1955
17L-7	VHF comm transmitter	1955-1975
51X-3	nav/comm receiver	1956
AN/TRC-68	UHF transportable comm	1956-1964
ASQ-19,37,56,58, 82,88	CNI system for Air Force	1956-1983
340D-1	passenger address amplifier	1956-1980
621A-1	ATC transponder	1956-1957
344B-1	VOR instrumentation	1956-1962
WP-103	weather radar	1956-1965
621A-2	ATC transponder	1956-1962
DN-101	Doppler navigator	1956-1965
NC-103	Doppler navigation computer	1956-1965
AP-103	autopilot	1956-1972
DF-202	automatic direction finder (ADF)	1956-1963
860E-1	distance measuring equipment (DME)	1956-1963
KWM-1	amateur transceiver	1957-1976
AN/ARC-58	HF airborne comm	1957-1978
AN/PRC-41	UHF packset radio	1958-1972
51Z ( )	marker beacon receiver	1958-1969
51RV-1	VOR/ILS receiver	1958-1970
AN/ARC 80	HF sentry radio	1959 1977
51S-1	HF receiver	1959-1972
618T	HF comm transceiver	1959-1982
51Y-4	automatic direction finder (ADF)	1959-1983
FD-105	flight director	1960-1983
621A-3	ATC transponder	1960-1973
51V-4	glideslope receiver	1960-1980
618M-1	VHF comm transmitter	1960-1975
DF-203	automatic direction finder (ADF)	1960-1974
URG-I/II	HF radio set groups	1960-1978
860E-2	distance measuring equipment (DME)	1961-1976
C-8400	computer system	1961-1965
51R-6	VOR/LOC receiver	1961-1981
51Z-4	marker beacon receiver	1961-1983
	X-15, Mercury, Gemini, Apollo, comm equip	1962-1972
AN/ARC-109	VHF airborne comm	1963-1976
642C-1	cockpit voice recorder	1963-1981
AL-101	radio altimeter	1963-1980
FD-108	flight director	1965-1983
621A-6	ATC transponder	1965-1978
346D-1B	passenger address amplifier	1965-1979
860F-1	radio altimeter	1965-1981

Type No.	Description	
618M-2	VHF comm transceiver	1965-1980
51RV-2	VOR/ILS receiver	1965-1981
C-8500	computer system	1966-1972
WP-104	weather radar	1966-1967
FD-105	helicopter flight director	1966-1967
LRN-104	Loran C receiver	1966-1968
51Y-7	automatic direction finder (ADF)	1967-1983
860E-3	distance measuring equipment (DME)	1967-1978
718U	HF transceiver family	1967-1983
INS-60/61	inertial navigation	1968-1975
FCS-110	flight control system	1968-1974
ANS-70	area navigation	1968-1982
ILS-70	ILS receiver	1969-1983
651S-1	HF receiver	1969-1980
FD-109/ASQ-141	integrated flight director	1969-1983
ALT-50	radio altimeter	1969-1983
TDR-90	transponder	1969-1983
DME-40	distance measuring equipment (DME)	1969-1983
VIR-30	VOR/ILS receiver	1969-1983
FD-110	flight director	1970-1983
AN/ARC-153/157	HF high performance radio sets	1970-1979
AP-105	autopilot	1971-1973
VHF-20	VHF comm transceiver	1971-1973
719D/PRC-515	HF transceiver family	1971-1982
DF-206	automatic direction finder (ADF)	1971-1983
621A-6	ATC transponder	1972-1983
618M-3	VHF comm transceiver	1972-1983
FD-112	flight director	1972-1974
AN/ARC-159	UHF airborne transceiver	1972-1974
ARN-108	ILS receiver	1972-1983
ARN-118	TACAN development & manufacture	1972-1983
	Galaxy system	1973-1983
AP-107	autopilot	1973-1975
AP-106	autopilot	1973-1975
AN/GRC-171	UHF AM/FM transceiver family	1973-1983
DF-301E	automatic direction finder (ADF)	1973-1983
HSI	horizon situation indicator (Space Shuttle)	1973-1983
FD-112	flight director	1974-1983
GPS	GPS user equipment	1974-1983
860E-4,5	distance measuring equipment (DME)	1974-1983
NCS-31	area navigation system	1974-1983
5IRV-4	VOR/ILS receiver	1975-1983
VHF-251	VHF communications transceiver	1975-1983
VIR-351	navigation receiver	1975-1983
IND-351	VOR/LOC course indicator	1975-1983

Type No.	Description	
GLS-350	glideslope receiver	1975-1983
AUD-250	audio center	1975-1983
PWC-150	power converter	1975-1983
HF-80	multipurpose HF comm systems	1976-1983
ADF-650	automatic direction finder (ADF)	1976-1983
TDR-950	ATC transponder	1976-1983
WXR-150	weather radar system	1976-1983
WXR-200	weather radar system	1976-1983
ADF-60	automatic direction finder (ADF)	1976-1983
HF-121,122	HF high performance radio sets	1977-1983
346D-2B	passenger address amplifier	1977-1983
DME-451	distance measuring equipment	1977-1983
ANS-351	area navigation system	1977-1983
APS-80	autopilot system	1977-1983
WXR-250	weather radar system	1977-1983
FCS-240	digital flight control system	1978-1983
DCE-400	distance computing equipment	1978-1980
628T-1	HF transceiver	1978-1983
AN/GRC-211	VHF AM multichannel transceivers	1978-1983
AL-104	radio altimeter	1978-1983
860F-4	radio altimeter	1978-1983
ACS-240	active control system	1978-1983
HSI-84	horizontal situation indicator	1978-1983
ADI-84	attitude director indicator	1978-1983
ADS-80	air data system	1978-1983
ARN-139	first airborne TACAN range & bearing	1978-1983
ARC-186	VHF AM/FM comm	1978-1983
AN/ARC-182	multi-mode UHF-VHF airborne transceiver	1979-1983
ADF-650A	automatic direction finder (ADF)	1979-1983
ADI-85	attitude director indicator	1979-1983
APS-841	helicopter autopilot system	1979-1983
FPA-80	flight profile advisory	1979-1983
HSI-70	horizontal situation indicator	1979-1983
ADI-70	attitude director indicator	1979-1983
HSI-85	horizontal situation indicator	1979-1983
HF-200	high frequency communications transceiver	1979-1983
KWM-380	amateur transceiver	1979-1983
LRN-70,80	long-range navigation systems	1979-1983
WXR-300	weather radar system	1979-1983
ILS-700	ILS receiver	1979-1983
VOR-700	VOR receiver	1979-1983
ADF-700	automatic direction finder (ADF)	1979-1983
LRN-85	long-range navigation system	1980-1983
RNS-300	radar navigation system	1980-1983
HF-220	HF communications transceiver	1980-1983

Fifty years of Collins products

Type No.	Description	
HF-380	commercial transceiver	1980-1983
AN/ARC-190	HF airborne comm system	1980-1983
JTIDS	USAF anti-jam comm development	1980-1983
TPR-700	ATC transponder	1981-1983
LRN-700	long-range navigation	1981-1983
LRA-700	low-range radio altimeter	1981-1983
PAU-700	passenger address amplifier	1981-1983
VHF-700	VHF transceiver	1981-1983
HFS-700	HF transceiver	1981-1983
FCS-700	flight control system	1981-1983
EFIS-700	electronic flight instrument system	1981-1983
VNI-80	vertical navigation indicator	1981-1983
ANS-31C	area navigation system	1981-1983
FMS-90	flight management system	1981-1983
EICAS-700	electronic crew alert and warning system	1981-1983
VP-100	voice privacy device	1981-1983
VHF-253	VHF communications transceiver	1982-1983
WXR-220	weather radar system	1982-1983
WXR-270	weather radar system	1982-1983
EHSI-74	electronic horizontal situation indicator	1982-1983
EFIS-86	electronic flight instrument system	1982-1983
MP-83	transportable comm	1982-1983
	B-1 intercom & flight director computer development	1982-1983
AHS-85	attitude heading reference system	1983
APS-85	autopilot system	1983
MCS-65	magnetic compass system	1983
APS-65	autopilot system	1983
EFIS-85	electronic flight instrument system	1983
PAC-200	probe antenna coupler	1983
DME-42	distance measuring equipment	1983
VIR-32	navigation receiver	1983
VHF-22	VHF communications transceiver	1983
WXR-700	Doppler turbulence detection radar	1983
DL-700	airborne data link	1983

Bibliography

Adelson, James. Interview, 1983.

Anderson, William G. Interviews, 1983.

American Aviation, August 6, 1951. November 26, 1951. January 5, 1983.

American Exporter, February 1947.

Annual reports of the Collins Radio Company, 1945 through 1973.

"Around the World in 99 Waypoints." *Flying Magazine,* May 1980.

Aviation Week, December 3, 1951. August 25, 1952. September 1, 1952. November 17, 1952. March 16, 1953.

"Battle for Survival." *Forbes,* December 1, 1970.

Betts, J.A., *High Frequency Communications.* American Elsevier Publishing Company, 1967.

Bourne, Kenneth M., "HF SSB System Perfected at Collins Liberty Station." *Communications News,* August 1974.

Broadcasting, April 10, 1950.

Bulkeley, William M., "The Fall and Rise: How Rockwell Aided Collins Radio Rebound." *The Wall Street Journal,* March 19, 1973.

"Can It Brew Coffee?" *Rotor & Wing International,* December 1980.

Cedar Rapids Gazette, various articles.

Chicago Journal of Commerce, December 26, 1947.

Clements, Ralph, *Tales of the Town; Little Known Anecdotes of Life in Cedar Rapids,* Stamats Publishing Company, 1967.

"Climbing Backlog Sparks Gains for Collins Radio." *Barron's,* March 13, 1967.

Collins Column, Collins Radio Company, various articles.

"Collins Radio Has $100 Million Backlog," *Barron's,* February 19, 1951.

Collins Signal, Collins Radio Company, various articles.

"Collins of Collins Radio." *Forbes,* January 15, 1964.

Collins, Arthur A., "Full Details of a Short Wave Transmitter." *Radio Age,* May 1926.

Collins, Arthur A., Speech before the Institute of Radio Engineers, September, 1952.

Colton, Russell. Interviews, 1983.

Communications, April 1948. March 1949.

Culver, Senator John, "A Continuing Success Story for Collins Radio." *Congressional Record,* October 6, 1978.

Danek, Ernie, *Tall Corn and High Technology,* Windsor Publications, 1980.

Davenport Democrat, December 21, 1947.

Des Moines Register, December 12, 1965.

Doelz, M.L., and J.C. Hathaway, "Mechanical Filter."

Electronic Industries, February 1945.

Electronics, July 1940. October 1951.

Ewoldt, Harold. Interview, 1983.

FM and Television, May 1949.

Fischer, Albert, "Flight Cancelled . . ." *Interavia,* Volume IX, No. 4, 1954.

Fishwald, Bruce, "What Goes On at a Corporation's Meeting?" *The Cedar Rapids Gazette,* November 20, 1963.

Flight, August 1952. January 1953.

Forbes, January 1968.

Fruehling, Tom, "Rockwell to Add $8.4 Million Building." *Cedar Rapids Gazette,* August 6, 1978.

Gates, Robert S., Speech before the New York Society of Security Analysts, September 15, 1960.

"Genius at Work." *Time,* September 24, 1956.

Gerks, Irvin H. Interview, 1983.

Goetz, John. Interviews, 1983.

Goodyear, Arlo, *The Collins Story,* October 14, 1954.

Gould, Jack, "New Radio Signal Opens Door to Global Video." *New York Times,* April 30, 1952.

"Guglielmo Marconi." *The Wireless Engineer,* September 1937.

Harrison, Gertrude. Interview, 1983 "He Makes Tinkering Pay." *Business Week,* March 13, 1954.

Henningson, Mary. Interview, 1983.

Hoopes, Townsend, "Veteran Collins Pilot Bids Farewell To A Special Lady." *Cedar Rapids Gazette,* May 9, 1983.

Huebsch, Tony. Interviews, 1983.

Investor's Reader, March 4, 1959.

I.R.E. Bulletin, Los Angeles Section, 1953.

Joliet, Illinois Herald-News, October 9, 1952.

Kueter, Dale, "Anatomy of Economic Turnaround for Collins Radio." *Cedar Rapids, Gazette,* June 17, 1973. "Collins Name Lives On." *Cedar Rapids Gazette,* December 4, 1977. "Collins Wins Major Avionics Contract." *Cedar Rapids Gazette,* July 21, 1979.

Kuster, Joanne, "Collins Sets Pace with Four Expansions." *Iowa Development Commission Digest,* December 1977.

Lahr, Millie. Interview, 1983.

Lander, Clayton. Interview, 1983.

Larson, Dorothy. Interview, 1983.

"Latest Search for Northwest Passage: The Plan, the Odds." *U.S. News & World Report,* May 12, 1969.

Lehman, Milton, *This High Man, The Life of Robert H. Goddard.* Farrar, Straus and Company, 1963.

Lippisch, George. Interview, 1983.

Lund, Merrill. Interview by Wilma Shadle, 1980.

Lyon, Evelyn. Interview, 1983.

Marriner, Ed, "The Story of Collins Radio." *CQ Magazine,* August 1965.

Marvin, Keith, *The Iowa Engineer,* November 1949.

McClellan, J. Mac, "VLF/Omega + Vortac = Practical Automatic Navigation." *Business and Commercial Aviation,* December 1980.

Metz, Robert, "Collins Versus the Middle Man." *The New York Times,* April 24, 1969.

Meyer, Dan, "Advancing Communications Research Through an Echo." *Collins Signal,* No. 4, 1960.

"Microwave Relay Replacing Cables," *New York Times,* March 21, 1954.

Miller, James. Interview, 1983.

Myers, Tom, "New Electronics Firm to Provide Jobs for 300." *Today,* June 13, 1976.

Nagle, James J., "Personality: An Inventor Dislikes Publicity." *The New York Times,* October 1, 1961.

News releases, Collins Radio Company and Collins Divisions of Rockwell International.

Nicholson, Gordon. Interview, 1983.

Nyquist, John. Interview, 1983.

Opfer, Norman. Interview, 1983.

Ottumwa Courier, July 4, 1938.

Ozburn, Jiggs, "The Collins Radio That I Knew." World Radio News, September 1973.

Pappenfus E.W., Warren B. Bruene, and E.O. Schoenike, *Single Sideband Principles and Circuits.* McGraw-Hill, 1964.

Pappenfus, E.W., "SSB — A Revolution in Emission." *Collins Signal,* Summer 1956.

Pearlstine, Norman, "Collins Radio Slates Computer Venture." *The Wall Street Journal,* September 6, 1968. "Collins Radio Hits Electronic Data's Take-Over Offer." *The Wall Street Journal,* April 1, 1969. "Tale of a Tender," *The Wall Street Journal,* May 8, 1969.

Peters, Leonard. Interview, 1983.

Pickering, Richard. Interview, 1983.

Plummer, Rick, "Comm Central Audio Visual Presentation." September 1, 1979. Interview with Henry Nemec.

Proceedings of the Board of Directors, Collins Radio Company, 1933 through 1945.

Prospectus for the Issue of Common Stock, 1944.

Pulse, Collins Radio Company.

Radio Craft, January 1947.

Radio and Television News, September 1951.

"Radio." *The New Encyclopedia Brittanica,* 1974.

Reiniger, Scott H., "New Picture Aid for ILS — Omnirange." *Aviation Week,* July 2, 1951.

"Rockwell's Surprising Winner: Collins Radio." *Business Week,* November 15, 1976.

Schweighofer, Horst M., "Flight Director," *Flug Revue,* October 1976.

Short Wave Craft, June-July 1930.

Signal, Journal of the Armed Forces Communications Association, July-August 1951.

Simbro, William, "A Strengthened Collins Aids Now-ailing Parent." Des Moines Sunday Register, January 11, 1976.

Skyways, December 1952.

Snodgrass, Al. Interview, 1983.

Soukup, Milo. Interviews, 1983.

Staehle, John D., *Collins Radio Company,* research paper, 1974.

Stearns, Ben. Interview with Arlo Goodyear, 1963.

Tibor, R.J., "Flight Deck Design — A Look Back Into the Past." Collins Air Transport Division, Rockwell International, 1982.

Wall Street Journal, May 7, 1952. October 9, 1952.

Walsh, Raymond, "Collins Collision Avoidance System." 1983.

Western Aviation, August 1951.

Williams, Ron, "Collins Has Systems Angle in Computer." *Electronic News,* May 5, 1969.

Wilson, Robert C., "A Message to Employees of Collins Radio Company." February 13, 1974.

Wilson, Robert C., "Presentation to Security Analysts." April 1972. "Presentation to Security Analysts." April 1973.

Zook, Nancy Gibbons, "Collins and the Electronic Beanstalk." *The Iowan,* March 1956.

Main Plant on 35th Street in Cedar Rapids houses office and factory space for the Collins Telecommunications Products Division. 1978 photo.